A
Roaring
Silence

A
Roaring
Silence

Or: How to Stop Worrying
and Learn How to Cope With Tinnitus

Frode Singsaas

ORANGE *frazer* PRESS
Wilmington, Ohio

Published for the author by:
Orange Frazer Press
P.O. Box 214
Wilmington, OH 45177
Telephone: 937.382.3196
For price and shipping information.
Website: www.orangefrazer.com

Book and cover design: Kelly Schutte and Orange Frazer Press

Painting of the ear courtesy of Knut Løvås

Library of Congress Control Number: 2019939404

Second Printing

This one's for you.

Table of Contents

Author's Note

Before you start reading, a word of warning. If you Google "Tinnitus" you most likely will find the following or similar descriptions of the condition. According to Wikipedia.org:

> *Tinnitus is the hearing of sound when no external sound is present. While often described as a ringing, it may also sound like a clicking, hiss or roaring. The sound may be soft or loud, low pitch or high pitch and appear to be coming from one ear or both. In some people, the sound causes depression or anxiety and can interfere with concentration.*

That doesn't sound too bad, does it? It's just a sound, a ringing in your ears. We all have experienced ringing in our ears from time to time. Be it from a concert, construction work or from the sound of a jet plane revving its engines. It's that high pitched noise that is present for just a few minutes or maybe an hour. Slightly annoying, but not something that you worry about because it's going to disappear by itself soon.

But what if it doesn't? What if instead of disappearing it keeps increasing in both volume and pitch? And what if, in addition to this, it adds a whole batch of other sounds such as clicking, hisses, and wails? And what if these sounds don't vanish by themselves? What if they are here to stay for all eternity?

Then what? Is it still "just a sound" or has it become something else entirely?

Frode Singsaas

"In some people, the sound causes depression or anxiety and can interfere with concentration," Wikipedia concludes.

The article understates what is without a doubt the most crucial factor about tinnitus. It makes it seem like the depression and anxiety is just a side effect that "some" tinnitus sufferers experience. Most people tend to think that it is the sound itself that is the main problem with tinnitus. It isn't. The main problem is that the fear and anxiety take over your life because you start to obsess over this sound in your head (tinnitus is not a sound in your ears, but a neurological disorder, a "brain sound" if you will, but much more on that later).

But then again, the term "some people" is also correct. This is because the majority of people afflicted with this condition do not experience depression or anxiety. For them it is a small annoyance that they brush aside and one that doesn't interfere with their quality of life in any significant way.

Just how many are tinnitus "sufferers" and how many are simply indifferent to this whole phenomenon is very difficult to ascertain. There are too many unrecorded cases of tinnitus because those who are indifferent to the sound in their ears don't make doctor appointments.

Adding more confusion and misery to this condition that already has made you a tinnitus sufferer, your first visit to your general practitioner (GP) will probably add another layer of distress to your anxiety. This is because most GPs don't know much about tinnitus. In fact, very few people know much about tinnitus at all because, in most cases where there's no noise exposure involved, nobody really knows what causes tinnitus or how to treat it. It's a mystery.

My tinnitus has been my faithful companion for the better part of six years now. At first, I was convinced that my life was over. I was at my lowest point, and I wasn't sure I could go on living this way.

Today I'm fine with my tinnitus. It makes the same sounds and is the same volume as it was on that day back in 2012, but it doesn't bother me anymore. How come? It all boils down to this one word—habituation.

I found a way out of this quagmire of misery and got my life back. And I want to share all I've learned from these past six years with you.

Everything I write on these pages is a result of my personal experiences with tinnitus, tinnitus-habituation and how to deal with the anxiety, the fear and the depression that so often comes with this peculiar and asinine condition. I hope that my story and the advice I offer here can provide some comfort for new *tinnitusians* (not a word yet, but one of these days the editors of Merriam-Webster or Encyclopedia Britannica have to get back to me on this...).

I owe a thousand thank yous to the members of the Tinnitus Support Message Board. Without the wisdom, support, and kindness of the veterans there, this book would never have been written.

I don't claim that this book can "cure" your tinnitus. There is no "cure" for tinnitus. But there is something just as good.

This book is about my journey that started on November 13, 2012, when in a matter of a few hours I became a knot of fear and anxiety that almost drove me to suicide. Those intense emotions ended three years later when the mystery of tinnitus finally revealed itself to me.

This book does not deal with the clinical or technical side of tinnitus. This is a tale that deals exclusively with the emotional part of this condition. What I'm hoping to achieve is to teach you what I have learned about coming to terms with this strange condition. How to cope with this bizarre noise in our heads.

My personal journey through tinnitus-hell is just that— personal. But I do believe that the process of habituation is somewhat similar for every tinnitusian.

You won't be stuck with this angry wasp in your head for the rest of your life. I promise. Read on, and I'll do my best to ease your mind.

Preface

You are a hero. You may not know it yet, but you are. We all are the heroes in our own stories, but the task you are about to undertake will genuinely make you a hero.

This may very well be the most significant achievement in your life. And the hardest. But the reward at the end is worth the struggle.

Unless you face or have faced an illness of grave proportions, tinnitus is most likely the worst thing that has happened to you so far in life. And all the suffering you're experiencing right now seems to stretch on forever. But it won't last and some miles down the road you will be fine.

And that's a promise. Let's start, shall we?

So, you have this annoying sound in your head, huh? I have one as well. I have a whole bunch of them. On a good day, they sound like a mix between a deranged banshee on psychedelics, a 747 revving its engines, and the whistling of a boiling teapot.

"It's so annoying," I hear you say.

Yes! Not just annoying. It is torture. A kind of pain that never ends. It's a sound like no other sound. It's a sound that makes your life miserable. And furthermore, it's a sound that is slowly driving you insane, keeping you awake at night and makes you act like a zombie. But you will recover.

You don't believe me? Of course you don't. And why should you? I know I wouldn't. Even if I could go back in time and read these very words. But that's alright. I'll make a believer out of you.

Frode Singsaas

This book won't make your tinnitus go away. But it can help ease your fear and anxiety. There will come a day when this noise in your head will no longer make your life miserable. It's not like you have anything to lose by reading on.

The following conversation took place at my otolaryngologist's office (my ENT physician) on January 3, 2013:

"So how are we today?"

"Miserable. My ears won't stop playing Lou Reed's *Metal Machine Music* on repeat." (Infamous rock album containing non-stop feedback).

"Quite bad, is it?"

"I'm in agony."

"OK. Let's see what we have here."

Here an assortment of strange apparatuses of unknown origin were shoved up my nose and down my throat.

"Nothing wrong with your ears."

"Come again?"

"Nothing wrong. Not as far as I can tell."

"But...but the noises in my ears? Why...what are they?"

"It's tinnitus."

"It can't be!"

"Well, it is. Trust me. I should know."

"But my GP was sure it was eustachian tube disorder."

"Eustachian, schmustachian.... Nah. It's tinnitus."

"But how can I get rid of it?"

"You can't."

"Seriously?"

"Yes. Funny thing this. Fascinating. For most people, tinnitus is a chronic condition. You'll probably have it for life."

"For life? You must be kidding?"

"Afraid not. Some of my tinnitus patients won't even go outside for fear that it will make the noise worse."

"But does it?"

"Does what?"

"Make it worse? Going out, I mean."

"Damned if I know."

"But there has to be something you can do?"

"No, not really. But if you'll excuse me. I'm already late for a lunch appointment, so if you will be so kind as to leave my office...."

We will get back to this conversation later, but for now, think of it as an hors-d'oeuvre for things to come.

A
Roaring
Silence

The Fire Alarm

On November 13, 2012, at 11am, the fire alarm went off at work. I got up from my desk, grabbed my jacket and headed for the door. For some reason, my co-workers didn't seem to react to the sound at all. This puzzled me a bit because we were drilled to leave the building immediately when the alarm went off, but I thought little of it at the time. The fire alarm had gone off at regular intervals the last six months due to endless testing and fire drills, so it was not like the building was on fire or anything like that.

But as I was about to descend the stairs, I paused for a second. Still nobody? How peculiar. I took a step down, then another one and froze.

The fire alarm had never sounded this high pitched before, had it? Or so multiphonic?

Then it hit me. The sound. It was inside my head. It wasn't the fire alarm. It was inside my head!

What the hell?

The pitch and the volume of the noise were deafening. I couldn't make out any other sound at all. All I heard was this insane CRACKLE-CRACKLE-TWEET-TWEET-WHEEEIIIIZUUUUUUZZZZ that seemed to come from somewhere inside my left ear.

Standing in the stairway, I tried to block both my ears by putting a finger in each of them.

But the sound was only getting louder.

What was this? What on earth was this?

I have almost no recollection from the next few hours. I remember getting in my car, but I don't remember the drive home or what I did the remaining hours of the day until my wife got home from work at midnight.

"I have this high-pitched noise in my ears," I said. "It's driving me crazy. It's so loud and obnoxious, and I don't know what to do about it."

My wife is a trained nurse. Surely she would know what was going on. She had nursed me through countless colds, cases of flu and headaches. One time she even gave me a band-aid when I'd cut my myself on a particularly vicious piece of paper.

"It is probably just ear wax," she said. "I told you to flush out your ears at least a thousand times." (No exaggeration this, she had told me a thousand times, I've counted.)

"But it came just out of the blue when I was at work," I said. "I'm in agony. It is crazy loud."

"Alright, I'll drive down to the pharmacy to get you some mineral oil and a soft bulb washer."

Thirty minutes later she was back.

"Are you sure this is the right equipment?" I asked. "It looks like some medieval torture instrument left behind by the Spanish Inquisition."

"Quite sure," she said. "Now come with me."

In the bathroom, she told me to take off my shirt and to tilt my head sideways. A warm and sticky sensation filled my ear and all of a sudden everything sounded muffled and distant.

"Now your other ear," she said.

"What?!" I shouted.

"Your other ear."

"Your lover's here?"

For some unknown reason, I got a slap on the head.

Then I went deaf. The oil in my ear sounded like a volcano on the brink of eruption. A sound that was replaced by a thunderstorm when she started shooting tepid water into my ears. I could still hear the howling banshee, but I was so confident that she could fix this thing that I managed to relax.

"Now get over here and bend over the sink with your left ear up."

A few minutes later an impressive amount of soft yellowy brown ear wax was busy scurrying around in our bathroom sink. My ears felt like they had been beaten with an ugly stick, but my hearing was of the sort you only read about in superhero comics. For a second there I was planning the costume I would wear when I was swishing and swooshing round town as "The Moth." I could still hear a low humming in my ears, but the deranged banshee was gone.

"You are a genius!" I said. "The crazy noise is gone. It's gone!" I planted a generous kiss on my wife's forehead and told her how much I loved her.

Half an hour later my wife found me sitting on the kitchen floor weeping. The sound was back with a vengeance, and now it was in my right ear also. Just as loud, but an octave higher. Imagine a piccolo flute playing a B sharp while a

Frode Singsaas

small orchestra of mixed bagpipes are playing G sharp at the same time, and you have the first ingredients of the sound. Then you add a couple of Norwegian black metal bands, a deranged soprano on amphetamine singing the theme to *The Exorcist*, and you have some idea of the lay of the land. Then you do a Spinal Tap and turn it up to 11.

"Is it back?" My wife asked. This time with some genuine worry in her voice.

"Yes, and it's even worse now," I sobbed uncontrollably.

"We better get you to a doctor," she said.

That night I lay awake moaning like a sick puppy. The volume of my iPad was turned up to eleven with a YouTube video of "Rain on the Tarmac" on repeat. Occasionally I would put on "Tropical Rainstorm" or "Ten hours of ocean waves crashing onto the shore" just to get some diversity. I had one hope, though. That this screaming, deranged banshee in my head somehow was going to disappear during the night. Now, if only I could sleep...

An Apple a Day Won't Keep the Doctor Away

I must have fallen asleep at some point because the sheets were soaking wet when my wife woke me early the next day.

"How do you feel?" She asked. "Do you want coffee?"

For just a second, I couldn't hear the sound. For a second. Then it came rushing back in all its glory.

"It is still there," I said. "Just as bad as it was yesterday."

"Loud?"

I nodded.

"Well, get up. The doctor's office opens in thirty minutes. You have to call the minute they open to be able to get an appointment later today."

How long did I sleep? It couldn't possibly have been more than an hour at most. I remembered that "Ten hours of ocean waves crashing onto the shore" soundtrack had begun to lose its novelty by the second hour. I must have fallen asleep during "Nature's Greatest Hits: Songs of the Humpback Whale."

A peculiar and slightly ironic aspect of tinnitus for most of us is the fact that the sound of running water, and in particular, a shower, can mask the noise partly or entirely. A discovery I made just a few minutes later.

"Oh, my God! It's gone!" I screamed in the shower. "Darling! Come downstairs. It is the most fantastic thing. I...."

The minute I stepped out of the shower the sound was back. How in the name of Zeus, Odin, Jupiter, Osiris and an assortment of other ancient deities was this possible? It was gone, and then it was back?

"Yes, dear?" said my wife with the look on her face she usually reserved for those special occasions when I say something stupid and moronic (which happens far more often than I'm comfortable with, but that's beside the point here).

"It was gone," I said. "In the shower. It was gone. And then it came back."

"What do you mean it came back?" She asked.

I tossed the wet towel on the floor and leaned over the sink while trying to cover up the tears that were flooding my face. It was no use pretending. And with the tears came the sobbing. The sort of sobbing I would never have guessed myself capable of.

"Oh, God! This...thing," I said. "I can't cope. It is unbearable. It is agony. Why won't it go away? I don't get it. It's so bloody loud!"

My wife went silent. She had never before seen me in such a state of helplessness. She looked at me silently for a few seconds. Her husband of twenty-odd years was crying like a child on the bathroom floor.

"I don't know what to do or what to say," she said. "Let's get you dressed. You have to see the doctor today. If they try to put you on a waiting list, you have to insist."

A few hours later I sat in the waiting room at my local medical center. After working up a slightly nervous tension in my voice on the phone (it wasn't hard, I probably sounded like the Greek chorus from Medea), they finally agreed to squeeze me in between two other patients. I could tell the minute I walked through the door to the medical center that it was going to be a long wait, and prior experience had long since taught me that my regular doctor was never a stickler for punctuality.

Forty minutes went by and every second was pure agony.

"Next patient, please."

I felt a rush of euphoria as I walked to my doctor's office. Surely, he would know what was wrong with me.

Yes, of course, he would. A doctor. A man of the Hippocratic oath. Marvelous people these doctors. Knowledgeable too. I felt better already.

The next day I was popping antibiotics while doing my best to drown my sinuses with hydrocortisone spray. The doctor knew his way around this problem. It was something called Eustachian Tube Disorder. A couple of weeks on meds and it would go away. He would know, wouldn't he?

"Hmm....," said the man of the medical profession two weeks later. "So, it hasn't improved at all, you say? Still the same shrieking noise?"

I don't remember what I answered.

"I think we need a second opinion," he said. "I will make an appointment with an otolaryngologist on your behalf." He then made a pause and said the words that I dreaded the most. "Perhaps it's tinnitus?"

Frode Singsaas

I thought I knew despair. How little did I know? Christmas 2012 will for me always stand as the lowest period of my life. Here the freak-out phase began. I still had some hope that an ENT would fix this all-consuming sound in my head, but the suspicion that it was tinnitus was starting to take hold. Perhaps I should consider an exorcist? From the myriad of noises in my head, I was sure that I'd heard someone speaking in Latin from time to time. And who was this Damien Karras anyway?

At this point, I didn't know much about tinnitus, but the little I read on the internet made me want to curl up in a corner and die. Tinnitus is a condition that in most cases is chronic. Which means that it never goes away.

To live with this stupid sound in my head for the rest of my life? No, not happening. If it really was tinnitus, there had to be a cure. We put a man on the moon, right? Surely there had to be some remedy to get rid of a sound? There had to be!

Every single minute, every hour of every day from that moment I was thinking about the sound in my head. The questions were always the same. WHAT IS THIS?! and WHEN WILL IT STOP?!! But the third question about whether it would be gone tomorrow was no longer an issue. I knew it would still be there in the morning.

I remember so distinctly Boxing Day. On TV *Home Alone* had just finished its 114th rerun and I remember thinking all I wished for was to be able to enjoy both my life and my family again. I was a vegetable. The noise was unbearable. Every waking second was pure terror. An almost physical pain combined with an all-consuming fear. All I wanted was to get my life back. Nothing else was even of the slightest importance.

A Common Problem

Indulge me while I paraphrase Shakespeare's *Richard III*:

Now is the winter of my discontent. There would be no more glorious summers. Neither would the clouds that hang above my house ever dissolve to show clear blue sky once more. Dive, thoughts, down to my soul. Here despair comes.

January 3, brings us back to Dr. Ear-Nose-Throat, or Dr. Evil as he shall be known from this point going forward.

What follows is the second part of the conversation that took place in his office on January 3, 2013. (The first part appears in the preface.)

"Lunch!" I cried. "I don't give a toss about your lunch. I can't live like this. There is a psychotic witch residing inside my skull and she's having a house party for the ages. There must be something you can do?"

I must have spoken more loudly than I was aware of. An angry vein began to pulsate in Dr. Evil's right temple.

"Calm down," he said. "And for god's sake try to breathe. Your face is turning white. The sound in your head is a product of your brain. And it's not a sound per se. Most likely your brain is trying to compensate for the loss of some of the frequencies your ears no longer can hear. Now tell me, do you often attend loud rock concerts or in any other way expose yourself to loud noise?"

"No," I sobbed. "I work in an office. It's the quietest place on earth, and I never go to rock concerts anymore."

"I'm sorry," he said while not looking very sorry.

"There's not much I can do for you."

He then he made a pause before delivering the final blow: "There is no cure for tinnitus. You just have to learn to deal with it. And if you're contemplating suicide don't bother calling me for help. I'm not a psychiatrist, you know."

Have you ever had the feeling of complete rejection? Either from a girlfriend, boyfriend, your boss or your teacher. I mean the sort of denial that has left you to feel utterly worthless?

This was the exact feeling I had walking along the snowy streets of my hometown that freezing day in January. Not only had the esteemed representative from the Hippocratic community literary pushed me out the door, but he was in every way the least sympathetic person I have ever met. I still couldn't quite believe what he'd just said, but I knew it to be true. The contempt in his eyes for taking up his time for something so trivial as tinnitus made me feel both angry and guilty.

Between the curses I silently sent him, a single sentence looped continually in my mind:

It's tinnitus!
It's tinnitus!
It's tinnitus!

Here I will take a break from my story and let you in on a secret. If you, for some reason, are reading this while your skull is making its best impression of a steam hammer attacking an industrial vacuum cleaner, I want you to know the following before we continue:

It will get better. So much better.

I will also make you aware of the fact that only a small percentage of all people who has tinnitus are tinnitus sufferers. Studies show that all humans have tinnitus of varying degree. If you have ever taken a hearing test, you know what I mean. Sitting in that booth with a pair of huge sound canceling earphones on, waiting for those almost inaudible beeps, you hear all sorts of hisses, crackles, and hums that come out of nowhere. This is your natural "ear noise." Sounds that you are born with and are unaware of most of the time. Only in tranquil places are you able to hear them.

Pawel J. Jastreboff, PhD, ScD, MBA, one of the leading experts in the field of tinnitus says this about tinnitus:

> Tinnitus (ringing in the ears) is a common problem, affecting about 17% of the general population around the world (44 million people in the USA). It causes significant suffering in about 4% of the general population (10 million in the USA).

A study on tinnitus from 1953 by Morris F. Heller, MD and Moe Bergman, EdD called "Tinnitus Aurium in Normally Hearing Persons" concludes that everybody has tinnitus to some degree or other. It further strengthens the argument that we as humans are incapable of experiencing total silence.

In other words, we are all tinnitusians one way or another. But for the few of us that experience the trials and tribulations of tinnitus suffering, this condition can wreak havoc on our lives. And to make it even worse, it's a condition that someone who has never experienced tinnitus can never fully understand. Not until you have been bereft of your capability to enjoy the silence (to the degree to which we are capable of "hearing" silence, that is) can you fathom the effect it has on your overall well-being.

And let's dwell on those numbers for a minute. According to Jastreboff, tinnitus causes suffering in approximately 4% of all those who are inflicted with the condition.

Not a very large number, is it? This means that most people with tinnitus go about their daily business without any problems, even though they have varying degrees of this condition. They are not tinnitus sufferers, people with tinnitus to whom this sound doesn't negatively interfere with their lives.

But what about that 4% who suffers greatly?

Dr. Jastreboff believes that this might have something to do with the rapidly-evolving conditioned response. It can be described as a response that becomes associated with a previously unrelated stimulus as a result of pairing the stimulus with another stimulus frequently yielding the response.

Pretty heavy stuff and very hard to understand. And don't feel bad if all this goes right over your head. The inner workings of what causes tinnitus and why it's so hard to determine a common factor for what it really is, is not what this book is about. This book is about making you as a tinnitus sufferer feel better and to no longer care about the noise in your head.

Dr. Stephen M. Nagler, one of the leading tinnitus experts in the world and the man behind Atlanta Tinnitus Consultants, LLC, and former head of the American Tinnitus Association, agrees with Dr. Jastreboff on this question but adds that there is no way of knowing for sure. Nagler also refers to the following underlying problem when it comes to tinnitus and tinnitus research:

> The research community has yet to agree on exactly what tinnitus is. Moreover, the quality of those studies that attempt to conclude anything at all about treatment efficacy is uniformly abysmal in terms of reliability and verifiability. Indeed, when I used to discuss TRT (Tinnitus Retraining Therapy) with my own patients, I took great pains to say that the only sort of compelling thing about the studies (besides the fact that the model makes so much sense) is that while their quality is clearly substandard, there is such a quantity of substandard studies that it is tough to ignore.

The fact that the research community are not able to agree on what tinnitus is in the first place is bound to create both confusion and doubt about all types of "treatments" for this condition. It inevitably leads to several factions of tinnitus sufferers who cheer on their "team," be it habituation, the belief in a future cure or a myriad of (unproven) treatments from stem cell replacement to Hyperbaric Oxygen Therapy.

The answer to the question of why a minority of people with tinnitus suffers so much is a mystery even to the most dedicated researcher. The truth is that nobody knows for sure.

I'm not only a firm believer in the habituation process but also a living, breathing example of how successful it can be if you genuinely dedicate yourself to it. Furthermore, it's not like you have any other options, right? Methods like Tinnitus Retraining Therapy (TRT), Cognitive Behavioral Therapy (CBT), Neuromonics Tinnitus Treatment (NTT), Tinnitus Activities Treatment (TAT) and Mindfulness-Based Tinnitus Stress Reduction (MBTSR) are all just strategies to shorten the time of natural habituation. The primary goal for all these different therapies is to relieve the patients of some of the distress and suffering that comes with the onset of tinnitus.

There are some universal truths about tinnitus. These are all facts that people new to tinnitus often refuse to believe. More on that later. But you should know that the first few weeks or months after the onset of tinnitus is a particularly trying period for most tinnitus sufferers.

This phase is often referred to as the *freak-out stage* or *freak-out phase* by the tinnitus community, and usually lasts from one to three months. It's the period when you are running around like a headless chicken, trying to get rid of this insane noise in your head with all means possible. It's the period when you are desperately surfing the internet looking for a "cure" while simultaneously making appointments with chiropractors, homeopaths, osteopaths, holistic practitioners, witch doctors, and voodoo priests.

You just as well could throw all your money in the wishing well or start searching for the pot of gold at the rainbow's end.

But you have to get rid of this insane noise in your head. And you will do anything to make it happen.

Every tinnitus sufferer at this stage is driven by instinct and fear instead of rational thinking. There are some exceptions to this rule, but they are few and far between.

Trying to teach a new tinnitusian the logic of habituation, is like trying to teach a shark the benefits of veganism.

Obsessing Over the Sound

During the next six months, I learned first-hand what depression is. Where there previously was hope, now there was none. The absolute bleakness and despair that overwhelms you when you finally accept that the sounds in your head will never go away are like nothing you have ever known. It is all-consuming. Every second of every minute of every waking hour I thought about the noise in my head. There was nothing that could distract me for even the shortest time.

> In the midway of this our mortal life,
> I found me in a gloomy wood, astray
> Gone from the path direct: and e'en to tell
> It were no easy task, how savage wild
> That forest, how robust and rough its growth,
> Which to remember only, my dismay
> Renews, in bitterness not far from death.
> —Dante Alighieri, *Divine Comedy*

The opening lines of this famous narrative poem could just as well have been written on the welcome mat outside my door the following year. I couldn't believe there was no cure. I couldn't fathom there was nothing anybody could do that would make this insane noise in my head go away.

Work, family life, hobbies, interests, hunger, thirst, lust for life—all gone. I was hollow. A walking talking shell that once housed all my *joie de vivre*.

If you are a tinnitus sufferer, you tend to get obsessed with the sound. Most of us spend our days searching the internet for answers (or more futile: a cure). Best case scenario—you get some support from people who know what you are experiencing. But this is the information age, so instead of seeking advice face-to-face with another human being, we turn to the internet.

There's no doubt that the digital revolution has made the world a much easier place to gather information on most subjects, but when it comes to collecting data on a topic like tinnitus, the internet can be a double-edged sword.

The problem is that you are guaranteed to meet other tinnitus sufferers who are just as distressed as yourself, and this is precisely the type of people you should avoid at all costs at this stage. And they are most certainly not the kind of people you should seek advice from to ease your suffering.

Sooner or later you are bound to stumble across the term "habituation." At this point, you are so confused and miserable that you hardly give it another thought. But here's the thing, in whatever direction you look, you will find mention of this idiosyncratic word.

Habituation.

Habituation is in so many ways just a wrap-around for the term "you'll get used to it." Technically speaking it means that your brain can adjust to changes. This is called neuroplasticity. It refers to changes in neural pathways and synapses due to changes in behavior, the environment, neural processes, thinking, and emotions—as well as to changes resulting from bodily injury. It means that your brain and your body will gradually get used to this sound in your head, and by that stop treating it as a threat. As this happens, you will stop freaking out about your head sound and step by step stop caring about the noise.

It doesn't matter if this doesn't make sense right now. In time, you will understand what it means.

I know what you're thinking right now.

"So, when will this *neuroplastichabituationwhatever-thingy* happen to me?"

Some people habituate to their head sounds faster than others. But because the experience of tinnitus is different for everybody, it is impossible to answer that question in a satisfactory manner. Some people habituate in just a few months; others again need much more time. For me, it took over two years to experience any significant habituation.

"But I don't have one sound. I have many," you might say. It doesn't matter one bit. One sound or one hundred. There are as many variants of tinnitus as there are tinnitus sufferers. And a whole selection of different sounds doesn't make the prospect for habituation or the time frame for habituation any less likely or slower than a person with only one sound.

Here's a story for you. I spent the best part of two years obsessing over my tinnitus. Two years of my life wasted on fear, anxiety and useless research for relief and (if-I-should-be-so-lucky) a cure.

Six months ago, a friend of mine woke up one day with an insane ringing in his ears. The verdict? Tinnitus.

But the funny thing is, whereas I became a living wreck, a bundle of fear, depression, and anxiety, he never reacted to it negatively at all.

After a few days (yes, days) he completely forgot all about it. Does he still have the ringing, the buzzing, the screams, and the howling? Yes, he does. But it doesn't bother him.

As previously mentioned, most people who receive a visit from the tinnitus-monster are capable of not paying any attention to it almost from the start. Others again need some time and are only slightly affected by it. Then there are us. The sufferers. The ones who lie awake at night, climbing the walls, and mourning for the life that we (at this point) are sure we'll never get back.

If you are a tinnitus sufferer who spends your days and nights harvesting information on forums and support boards on the internet, you have probably come across the two camps of tinnitus sufferers. On one hand, you have those who believe in the logic of habituation. Let us call this group The Habituationers. On the other hand, you have those who believe in a cure. Modern medicine is bound to come up with something, right? Be it stem cells, drugs, surgery or Dr. Wilson's Magic Elixir. They are The Miracle Crew.

The Habituationers and The Miracle Crew have waged war on tinnitus forums on the internet since the dawn of the world wide web. I can only imagine how a brand-new tinnitus sufferer must experience this never-ending battle. Not only has your life been turned upside-down by this noise, but the ones you turn to for support are busy playing whack-a-mole with rhetoric.

After five years with this screaming banshee living inside my head, I have learned a thing or two. Most important, I have learned that there are a couple of undeniable truths about tinnitus.

1. There is no cure for tinnitus (not yet, anyway).

2. In most cases, nobody can tell you what caused it.

3. Most GPs, don't know the first thing about tinnitus.

I'm confident that if somebody found a cure for tinnitus, it would make front page news all over the world. I know for a fact that habituation is real. After almost three years of living hell and longing for relief, it finally came to me (as it will for you, too). You can argue that this makes me an advocate for The Habituationers. But I also understand what fuels The Miracle Crew's steadfast determination and spirit. If we were able to put a man on the moon as far back as 1969, surely we can come up with a cure for this nonsense? And perhaps we can. But we're not there yet. And in the meantime, we only have our brain to trust to deal with this thing.

You see, the reason you feel this way right now is that you fear the sound in your head. I also know that you are thinking to yourself that all this is nothing more than a cleverly disguised "miracle cure;" a cynical attempt to earn money on this book by pretending to know it all. The noise is so loud and so annoying that nobody in their right mind can live comfortably with it.

But you are dead wrong for thinking this. Not only do we who have habituated live comfortably with our head sounds, but some of us also have a better life than before tinnitus.

Intrigued?

Or do you think I'm lying through my teeth?

If so, I will prove you wrong.

But I'm getting ahead of myself. Let's first break it down to the main factors that stand in your way of habituation right now—the fear and anxiety.

Fear

There's this one thing that all tinnitus sufferers have in common—the fear. This fear manifests itself in a myriad of ways. First, there is the fear of never getting your old life back. Then there is the fear of the sound itself or the doubt that the head sound will never go away. Further down this list, you will find the fear that the noise itself will drive you insane, and the fear of losing your hearing.

The most important lesson you will learn is this: it's not the sound itself that makes your life miserable, it's the fear.

If you are a fresh tinnitus sufferer, this is the part where you probably will call me a liar. It's the noise that is causing you fear and anxiety. How can I claim otherwise? If it weren't for the sound, there wouldn't be a problem in the first place.

True.

But that doesn't make my statement any less correct. You see, there is a useless and annoying sound in your head. This sound makes you afraid because it's not supposed to be there. But what if we remove the fear from this situation? Almost impossible to imagine, right? Impossible because it's the sound that's making you afraid, depressed, and utterly miserable. But the thing is, this fear is a creation made by your brain. It's a phantom menace. And because your mind has detected an intruder, a threat to your wellbeing, it's alerting you to this so you can act on it. But you can't act on tinnitus, can you? So, it just keeps doing its thing, and your brain keeps on alerting you to this sound that it has classified as a major threat.

You can't battle your tinnitus (and I know you won't hear this) but in most cases, it's here to stay. But you can fight the fear. And if you manage to lose your fear, all that remains is an annoying sound that's not physically or mentally harmful.

What I'm saying is that you have to accept the fact that the fear and the anxiety will be your traveling companions for a while. Neither the fear or the anxiety can harm you physically or mentally. I know very well that they make your life miserable right now, but those feelings will fade. For the time being it's all about enduring all those feelings that make you cry yourself to sleep at night.

You can't "unhear" your tinnitus and you can't lose the fear in any meaningful way at this point. The only thing you can do is to ride it out. It will soon get better, but the first three months is where it's at when it comes to the biggest bumps in the road. All you can do now is to fight the noise with noise.

As all the Heavens were a Bell,
And Being, but an Ear,
And I, and Silence, some strange Race,
Wrecked, solitary, here –
        —Emily Dickinson,
          "I felt a Funeral, in my Brain"

Frode Singsaas

Fighting Sound With Sound

The only good thing my appointment with the ENT led to was a referral to an audiologist who also was one of the few certified tinnitus specialists in my city. One of the things that all tinnitus sufferers have in common during the freak-out phase is hope. Hope that there is someone out there who can cure this condition. My initial hopefulness had turned sour at this point, but I still felt the tingling sensation of optimism when I showed up for my first appointment. I mean, she was a specialist. Someone who finally knew all about tinnitus and maybe she knew what to do to make it go away.

During the freak-out phase, most of us need something to help us cope with the sound. Some of us get prescriptions for Xanax or other benzodiazepines. Others prefer to mask the noise.

Remember that only a small fraction of people with tinnitus comes under the group of "sufferers." Most people with tinnitus don't suffer at all. And it doesn't matter how loud or high pitched your tinnitus is. Neither does volume. One person can go entirely off the rails with just the slightest humming in one ear, while another won't even bother seeing the doctor at all, even if he or she has the sound of magnum sized asphalt drills punching holes through their eardrums.

If you live in a country with excellent health benefits, you can probably get some professional maskers from your ENT or your audiologist. Or if you are well off, you can buy a pair yourself (they tend to cost around €800 / $1,200). There is also a plethora of white noise apps for your smart phone ("Simply Rain" and "Simply Noise," both from Reactor LLC are two of the very best). I also recommend getting a white noise app on your phone that will match the pitch of your tinnitus. This way you don't have to turn the volume up. In my experience, if you can find a noise that matches your pitch perfectly, it will completely mask your head sound, even at very low volume.

But let's get back to the story.

The audiologist made it quite clear from the first moment of our discussion that there was no cure for tinnitus.

"There are coping techniques, though," she said. "The most common ones are Tinnitus Retraining Therapy and Cognitive Behavioral Therapy. I suggest a combination of the two together with maskers."

"Maskers?" I said, puzzled.

"Hearing aids," she said. "Hearing aids with white noise tuned to the pitch and volume of your tinnitus."

"But I don't have a problem with my hearing," I said. "It's just that I hear every sound through a veil of hoots, cackles, and wails."

"You do have a slight hearing loss," she said. "The hearing test revealed as much. But nothing out of the ordinary. In any case," she continued. "And you said it yourself, you don't work in a noisy environment, you haven't been to any loud venues lately, and you haven't had any problems with your ears except some cases of ear infection as a child. You told me that your tinnitus appeared out of nowhere, and I can't find any physical or mental reasons for it."

"But there has to be something that triggered it," I said.

"Not necessarily. In fact, in most cases, tinnitus just happens. It doesn't matter your age. It just happens. And where there are no external factors to pin it on, there is simply no way of telling why you got it. If you like, I will order a pair of maskers for you. And I suggest that you wear them at all times from now on."

Relief washed over me. The prospect of getting a pair of maskers that would cover up the banshee covenant that was squatting in my skull lifted my spirit a few notches. Back home I downloaded a variety of white noise apps on my smart phone, and set to work to find the one that matched the pitch of my tinnitus most accurately.

As I previously mentioned, there are hundreds of white noise apps on both the iTunes App Store and Google Play. Some of them are free. But as I was about to learn, not many are any good. What I soon discovered was that to best mask your tinnitus you have to nail down the exact pitch and tone of the sound in your head. But if your tinnitus is like mine, you don't have a single tone to mask, but a whole symphony orchestra. I finally settled for one of the most expensive ones. The embedded equalizer made it possible to match my tinnitus to the point that I no longer could hear it.

Now, this is one of the more peculiar things about tinnitus (and one that my audiologist made no mention of), but if you can match the pitch of your tinnitus with a similar frequency of noise, you will no longer be able to hear it. It doesn't matter if you turn the volume of the matching noise way down. So long as there is a match in pitch, it completely covers the sound of the noise in your head. Of course, you hear it again the minute you turn off the noise app, but for a few minutes or hours, you can escape the dreadful noise that is ruining your life.

This discovery made me feel like I'd found the Holy Grail. I was so excited that I jumped up and down in the living room while bursting out in song. But the excitement died as suddenly as it has appeared when I found out that it only worked without headphones.

The only way this pitch-perfect white noise covered the sound of my tinnitus was when it pumped its kooky tones through the tiny speakers of my phone. Any addition of bass or middle tone completely ruined the effect, and my tinnitus was once again the most dominating sound.

Much later, when I finally got my masker, I made a big mistake. What the audiologist didn't tell me was that the volume of the masker should not completely mask the sound of tinnitus, just a little below. I turned the sound of the maskers up so loud that when I removed them for the first time that night, my tinnitus came back with a vengeance. I didn't match the pitch, just the volume.

The Tinnitus Information Assembly

On the last day of January, 2013, I attended a class for tinnitus sufferers. The "class" or "information assembly," as my audiologist described it, was being led by one of my country's leading tinnitus experts: a doctor with more PhDs than I have socks. He was a thin, tall man who spoke with the confidence and arrogance you only find in people who've spent their whole lives in academic environments. If my ENT was the least sympathetic person I had ever met, this was his successor.

The classroom was packed with people of all ages. A man in his early 60s dressed in a taxi driver's uniform was constantly covering his ears. A teenage boy, just shy of his twentieth birthday, held his head down and cried silently throughout the entire meeting.

"Neuroplasticity is the brain's ability to reorganize itself by forming new neural connections throughout life," said the tinnitus expert.

"Neuroplasticity sometimes may also contribute to impairment," he continued. "For example, people who are deaf may suffer from a continual ringing in their ears, the result of the rewiring of brain cells starved for sound. For neurons to form beneficial connections, they must be correctly stimulated."

At this point, my mind started to wander. The last thing I needed to hear was yet another theoretical and academic explanation of what tinnitus was. I guess this was applicable to all the other tinnitusians in the room. I didn't care one bit about the inner workings of tinnitus. All I wanted to know was how to cope with this screaming banshee in my head. The "expert" kept it going for half an hour on plasticity and neural networks until the teenager in the back of the room got the courage to ask the one question everybody in the room was dying to know the answer to.

"Do you have tinnitus or have you ever experienced tinnitus yourself?"

"No, never. I have perfect hearing," said the doctor and continued his lecture on neural pathways and noise trauma without missing a beat.

I'd had enough. Strange how every expert on tinnitus, self-appointed or educated, never had suffered this condition themselves. My ENT first awoke this suspicion. My theory that most doctors had absolutely no idea how it actually felt to be a tinnitus sufferer, was slowly crawling its way towards being a fact. Most people know how a cold or a stint of influenza feels. They are both common conditions that most of us can relate to. But this? There's no way you can put yourself in a tinnitusian's shoes if you haven't experienced the total loss of silence and inner peace that comes with a constant sound in your head yourself. And it's not "just a sound." A sound is, in most cases, external.

This one is inside your skull.

There is, of course, an exception to this, for instance when you are crunching down on a biscuit. But to have a high-pitched sound inside your head 24/7 is a whole other ballgame. This is where the fight-or-flight mechanism comes into the picture. When you first get hit with tinnitus, all your instincts tell you to either run away from this dreadful sound or fight it. Of course, none of these actions are possible. Every waking hour you do all you can to fight this intruder.

I left the "tinnitus information assembly" with a nightmarish suspicion in my head that perhaps nobody knew much about tinnitus. Not even the "tinnitus experts."

Rock Bottom

Let's rewind the story a bit. My audiologist told me it would be a two- to four-week wait before my maskers would be delivered. It could just as well have been an eternity. Four weeks in the freak-out phase can seem like four months. But of course, it didn't take two weeks, or four weeks, not even five weeks. It took six weeks. And during that time, I was close to ending it all. You see, the worst time of any tinnitus cycle isn't when it first hits, and neither are the following weeks when you are running around like a headless chicken, making doctors appointments. No, the worst part is when it dawns on you that this noise really is for life.

Think about it for a while. There's this unbearable sound in your head. A sound so shrill and disturbing that it's almost like a physical entity. And it will never go away.

Never.

Ever.

This is when thoughts darker than you'd ever thought possible start knocking on your door. That's when you first start thinking seriously about the S-word.

Suicide.

This is the part where we have to start drilling down to the deepest and darkest place of the human mind. Pitch black. The winter of our discontent and so on. And with no son of York in sight for bloody miles.

When the idea of ending your own life first enters your brain, your first reaction is to ignore it. But it creeps back. Oh, so slowly, it keeps coming back.

Your inner conversation then goes something like this:

"I can't do it. I can't. What about my family? They will be devastated."

"Yes. Without a doubt. But how long can you stand this before you lose your mind?"

"I don't know. I'm trying to hang on, but it's so difficult."

"Yes, of course, it is. You can't sleep. You can't eat. Hells bells! You can't even interact with other people anymore, can you? And forget about sex. Sex is something that happens to other people."

"Why am I in such pain? Why won't this thing go away? This is no life. This isn't even a half-life. I feel like a vegetable. There is no joy in anything anymore. All I can think about is this noise in my head and why it won't go away."

"But you can end it."

"Yes, I can."

"But will you?"

"I don't know. I can't think straight anymore. This noise is unbearable. No, it's worse than unbearable. It's slowly killing me. The thought that I have to suffer through this the rest of my life is just unthinkable. I won't have it."

"Then you know what you'll have to do, don't you?"

You know that you have hit rock bottom when thoughts and imaginary conversations like these occupy your brain. But listen to me when I say that this is as bad as it gets. Right here is the waterline. Not your point of no return, but your point of return.

This is so important that I will repeat it:

This *is* your point of return.

Now it's the time you have to ask yourself this question:

So how can I deal with this newfound knowledge that I am going to have a noise in my head from now until the day I die?

It's unbearable. Right? You said so yourself. But if it's unbearable, how come that right now, at this exact moment, I'm sitting, quite calmly, at my kitchen table, writing these words? Sitting here typing, while there is a full force gale in my ears. How come I'm quite content, even though I can hear this deranged banshee on crack howling bloody murder in my head?

I'll tell you how. But first, let's get on with the story.

The day finally came when my audiologist called and asked me to see her.

"I know you asked for the blue ones," she said. "But they were all out. So, I got you these." She opened a box the size of a matchbox and pulled out a pair of very tiny sea shell looking gadgets.

"I guess you could call them some sort of brownish," she said. "I know they look kinda old school, but if you'd rather wait for the blue ones, I could..."

"I'll take them," I interrupted her. "I couldn't care less about the color. They could be pink with My Little Pony stamps on them for all I care. I'll take them."

"Okay," she said. "Let's get these buds fitted for you." She then proceeded to attach the maskers to my ears. "Now I need you to tell me when I hit the sweet spot," she said. "That means when I find the pitch that matches your tinnitus-sound the most."

"Go on," I said.

A few seconds later a rushing sound of white noise filled my ears. It was bliss. I could no longer hear the tinnitus at all.

"Is that it?" she said. "Does it match your own?"

"I don't know if it matches," I said. "But it feels great."

"Good," she said. "That's the point. Now let's try out some other frequencies."

Half an hour later I walked out of my audiologists' office. Tucked behind my ears I wore my new maskers with a sense of pride. I had three different sounds to choose from. A white noise, a pink noise and a brown noise. The rest of the day I took great pleasure in switching between them.

Turning It Up To 11

When you first experience getting your life pulled out from under your feet by tinnitus, you tend to lose some weight. During the first six months I transformed from a slightly overweight middle-aged man to something you rarely see outside of modern art galleries. I didn't just lose weight. I shed it. Like a kid sheds his jacket in the summer heat.

I've always had a weak spot for the pleasures of the dinner table. Not only that, but also for all sorts of chocolate, sodas, chips, and candy. When tinnitus first hit me, all those cravings went out the window.

The best thing you can say about tinnitus is that it is an efficient form of dieting. I wouldn't recommend it though.

Finally, I had my maskers which were able to give me some relief, and with that my appetite returned—in a big way. The following weeks I ate like a whale. Food started to taste good again and my newfound slender body changed into something that resembled a puffed blowfish after a heavy meal. After a few months I had gained all of my weight back—and then some.

The strange thing is that during that period, I started to find my maskers a bit annoying. What had given me relief during those first weeks, now failed to do so. I could hear the howling banshee clearly over both the brown and the pink noise. Only the white noise, if turned up to 11, was able to almost entirely mask the sound of my tinnitus (if you don't know the term of turning something up to 11, I highly suggest you watch the movie *This is Spinal Tap*). But now I had a different annoying sound to deal with—the noise from the maskers.

Sometimes it is difficult to determine what is the lesser of two evils. My tinnitus drove me slowly insane, but at the same time, the never-ending SSSSSHHHHWWWW-WOOOOSHSWIIIIIICHZZZZZ from the maskers made a pretty good try at beating my tinnitus at its own game.

Have you ever seen a decapitated chicken? They sometimes run around in circles. Literally a headless act. During these weeks and months, I was a headless chicken. Put the maskers on, take the maskers off. When the sound of my tinnitus threatened to make me climb the wall, I'd put the maskers on. When the sound from the maskers made me feel like I was living inside a waterfall, I'd take the maskers off. On and off. On and off. On and off—for months.

Finally, I concluded that no matter how atrocious the sound in my head was, the constant static noise from the maskers was worse.

During the second half of 2013 and most of 2014, I carried the maskers with me in my pocket. Just in case I needed them.

I seldom did.

Dealing With Anxiety

As previously mentioned, the first three to six months are generally considered to be the worst period of any tinnitusians life. At this point, I'd had tinnitus for eight months. A life sentence with an eternal swooshing, squeaking sound.

But whenever the night is dark and full of terrors (thanks George R.R. Martin) there is also a shimmer of light in the blackness of it all. And that light was a small book called *Anxiety No More* by the British author Paul Davis. Mr. Davis did not have tinnitus. I have to stress that point. But boy, did he know a thing or two about anxiety. And as you probably have figured out by now, tinnitus is all about the fear and anxiety associated with the sound, and not so much about the sound itself. And I had fear and anxiety enough to fill a dozen shipment containers.

Anyway, Mr. Davis' book dealt with anxiety in general terms and how to deal with it. It was a short book. I downloaded it on my phone and read it all in one sitting. In the days that followed, I found myself frequently going back to it, especially the chapter about facing one's own fear. For there was one particular sentence that struck a chord with me: "You have to face your fear," Mr. Davis wrote. Not a particularly original thought, perhaps but then came the punchline: "It's perfectly alright to feel miserable. In fact, you are allowed to feel miserable."

"Oh, really? Am I now?" I said to myself.

Okay. Maybe I should try just that? It couldn't possibly be any worse than it already was.

The next day I set out to allow myself to feel as miserable as I could. I tried as hard as I could to wallow in my misery. I allowed myself a degree for self-pitying that most likely would have won me a gold medal in a self-pitying contest. I swam in it. I basked in it. I was the most miserable man in the world.

But lo and behold, what happened? I started to laugh. For the first time in months, I actually started to laugh. At myself. It was impossible. And it was ludicrous. I mean, it was just a sound. A sound in my head. In no way a life-threatening sound. Just a sound.

And then it dawned on me; was I really to let this little bugger of a sound ruin my life? Sure, it was hard. And sure, it was agony, but really.... In the words of the late B.B. King, how blue could I get?

I decided from then on, I would allow myself to feel as miserable as my tinnitus wanted me to whenever necessary. It was not like it could get any worse.

A new chapter in my tinnitus suffering had started. The days of endurance.

Leaving On a Jet Plane

One month went by, then two. Slowly, oh so slowly the snow thawed away and spring returned to my fair country once more. April turned to May and May was soon brutishly pounded in the dust by June. Summer. Vacation time.

Nine months had passed since this unwelcome guest had moved into my head and it was time to set off for distant shores. In this case, the beautiful Spanish island of Majorca. Naturally, I was scared stiff by the thought of accompanying my tinnitus on a plane. I've read all the horror stories: flying makes your tinnitus worse, flying will get you nowhere (not true, it literally does), flying will make your ears fall off and make your head explode. For some reason flying and going to the dentist are every tinnitus sufferers' worst fears. But I'll let you in on a secret, flying doesn't affect your tinnitus at all. At least not in the case of the many other tinnitusians I have talked to prior to writing this book.

But I digress. The flight was delayed an excruciating five hours. Imagine my misery at the airport. Not only was the anxiety of flying making my blood pressure do its best to

Frode Singsaas

imitate a horny, young racehorse seeing a mare in heat for the first time, but I also had to deal with it in an airport lounge full of crying children who were bored out of their minds. Surely this would wake up the sleeping beast in my head. (My tinnitus was surprisingly mellow this day. I was convinced it was preparing for a full-blown attack.)

And when the call for departure finally came, I was walking on eggshells. I don't know if you have any experience with chartered trips, but they are usually filled with young families with toddlers and young children who are not afraid to speak their mind on a plane (an understatement for sure). The volume in the cabin was deafening.

"This is your captain calling," said a voice over the speaker system. "There is going to be some turbulence during the first part of the flight. But on the upside, the weather in Majorca is close to perfect. Relax and we will get you there in no time."

Alas! A five-hour flight with turbulence and screaming children. Perfect. Just perfect.

When the engines were revving and the plane gathered speed I was as stiff in my seat as a tin soldier, bracing for the impact of the tinnitus demon I was convinced was sitting on my shoulder biding his time.

Once we were in the air my tinnitus didn't seem to react in any way to either the altitude, the humming of the jet engines or the screaming children. I slowly started to relax a bit.

"Are you OK?" Asked my wife. "Your ears...?"

"No. I'm fine," I said. "Surprisingly."

"Good."

I continued to relax. OK. So, I had this crazy banshee on crack in my head. But at least she didn't seem to mind going away on holiday. Good for her. And good for me. For the first time in months, I was able to read a book while we waited for the inevitable plastic-tasting airline food. Things were looking up. My maskers were secure in my left pocket. I had with me an ample supply of batteries (truth be told, I had brought along enough cells for a trip to Mars and back), and I thought I might be able to enjoy myself a little bit in the coming days if my tinnitus would just let me have some time off.

My tinnitus is of the ever-changing kind. It fluctuates. On a bad "ear day," it's loud. I mean, really, really loud. On a good "ear day," the sound(s) take the form of some low electric crackle. Like the hiss from a power pole. And there is no way to tell if the volume is "objectively" louder on those good days. It's just...different.

When we hit the first patch of turbulence, I noticed a high-pitched scream starting to build up. Here we go, I thought, searching frantically in my pockets for my maskers.

"What are you doing?" Asked my wife.

"Must get the maskers on," I said. "My ears are starting to act up."

"High-pitched screams?"

"How did you know?"

"Turn around."

A second later I was face-to-face with a six-year-old pitching a hissy fit. Her face was one inch from mine, and she had the most high-pitched wailing I've ever heard. Her mother just looked at me indifferently and shrugged as if to say that there was nothing she could do. We hit another patch of turbulence and the kid (who wasn't fastened in her seat) hit her head resulting in her shrieks becoming even louder.

Frode Singsaas

"Aren't you glad we decided on this holiday?" My wife asked me with a smile on her face which I couldn't quite make out whether it was sarcastic or just pure evil.

"Couldn't be happier," I said while trying my best to ignore the cacophony of crying babies the six-year-old behind me undoubtedly had orchestrated in an act of sheer evil.

"Look at it this way," my wife said. "It can't possibly get any worse than this."

I had my doubts about that statement, but if life has taught me anything, it has taught me not every thought should be said aloud, so I kept my mouth shut for the rest of the flight.

Desperate Times Call for Desperate Measures

Looking back, I sometimes cringe at all the weird stuff I was doing to ease the suffering during my first year of T. But that's what tinnitus does to you. It makes you try out even the most bizarre things in the hope that it will ease the pain. Of course, as you later learn, nothing makes much difference.

But as the man said, "Life is stranger than shit," (Joe Minaldi, Sergio Leone's *Once upon a time in America*) and tinnitus is even stranger.

Here is a collection of strange things I used to do to try to soften my tinnitus during my first year. Needless to say, nothing made even an ounce of difference.

1. Listening to Hungarian talk radio, all day long.

I don't speak Hungarian. I don't know anyone who speaks Hungarian, and I don't know the first thing about Hungary. But one piece of advice I came across during my first year was to listen to talk radio in a language I couldn't understand. This was supposed to "train" my ears to ignore intruding sounds.

So, for about eight weeks, I listened to Hungarian talk radio every waking hour. Did it make me forget my T-suffering? Not at all. Did it bore me to tears? Frequently.

2. Turn on the faucet.

I learned during my first week of T that the sound of running water was the only thing that completely masked my tinnitus. To achieve this kind of masking I had to:

a.) Take a shower, or

b.) Stand in close proximity to a running faucet.

Now, these are two things that are quite challenging on a daily basis. There are only so many showers you can take each day (the water gets cold, and your skin gets kind of sloppy-looking).

My running to the bathroom, turning on the faucet and putting-my-head-down-in-the-sink ritual came to a natural end during my second week when I noticed that my wife had put the telephone number to the nearest psychiatric clinic on speed dial on her phone.

The compulsive showering lasted longer than I like to admit. It continued for three years. I don't know if this applies to every other tinnitusian, but for me, standing in the shower completely masks out the sound of my tinnitus. Go figure.

3. Try every vitamin known to man (and then some).

You have probably heard it or read it: Vitamin so-and-so can "cure" your tinnitus. Well, I decided I would leave no stone unturned, so I went out and bought enough vitamins to choke a horse. Vitamin A to Z, Ginkgo Biloba, Aloe Vera, Magnesium, extract of cow manure, tears from a virgin, hair from an old hag and so on. I probably would have tried to put blood leeches in my ears if I had found such advice somewhere. Luckily, I didn't. I stopped at saliva from a cursed goat.

I don't know what the vitamin industry think we humans are capable of swallowing, but some of these pills were large enough to plug a leaking oil tanker. But I kept calm and carried on. During my third month of tinnitus distress, I was so choked full of vitamins that I couldn't catch a cold even if I was to French kiss a pneumonia patient.

Did any of these vitamins do anything at all to change or diminish my suffering or the volume of my tinnitus? Of course not. But on the bright side, I haven't had a cold ever since.

4. Noise generators.

During my first night of tinnitus, I learned that the only remedy against intrusive tinnitus was sound. The only way I was able to get some sleep was with an iPad with (volume at 11) sound effects pressed against my ear. There are thousands of different sound/noise generators available for tablets and smart phones. Some of them good. Others...not so.

I eased my way in. Early favorites were "Rain on tarmac" and "A waterfall in a tropical forest." I later advanced to stuff like "Thunderstorms and rain clouds," "Automobile noise in the rain," and "24 hours of running water."

All these soon started to annoy me, because they didn't mask the sound completely. I then went on to stuff like "A field of cows," "Crazy crickets," "The song of the whales," and "101 popular Hungarian dance songs" (for some reason I still believed that Hungarian stuff was the key to it all).

This part of my bullet point list is the only one that works in some way for tinnitus relief. I no longer need any of this stuff, but it was a lifesaver during my darkest hours.

5. Don't drink/eat that!

I've been there. You have probably been there too. During the freak-out phase, we tend to listen to even the most asinine advice. Like: "do not drink coffee/tea, the caffeine makes your tinnitus even louder, and your eardrums will explode" or "Do not eat chicken, your tinnitus will react in the harshest possible way, and you will start to grow feathers."

Nonsense, of course. You can eat and drink what you like. For the longest time, I believed that wine would make my tinnitus louder. It did not.

6. Don't listen to music with headphones. It will make your tinnitus worse and make your ears fall off.

For six months I believed this too. I treated all headphones like Satan's spawn. I even made myself a wooden cross draped with clusters of garlic that I waved in the general direction of any headset I saw.

I mainly blamed Neil Young and Icelandic band Sigur Rós for my tinnitus (I listened to both of them the day the tinnitus struck—with headphones!).

Ironically, I later learned that Neil Young has tinnitus.

And of course, when I finally did man-up to put on a pair of headphones again, nothing happened. Nothing at all.

7. Early to bed.

For the first six months of my tinnitus journey, I went to bed as early as possible every night. If I stayed up past 10 pm it was an exception. I believed that if I got as much as 10–11 hours of sleep, the next day would be a good "ear day."

Why did I believe that? Because I read it somewhere on the internet. If I even had just a tiny bit of common sense at the time, I would have known that this wouldn't help at all.

I missed out on a lot of family time and social interactions because of this stupid, stupid belief of mine. This is the one I regret the most.

8. Looking for a cure.

Okay, *this* is the stupidest of them all. For most of the first year, I would search for a cure for tinnitus 24/7.

I tried the following alternative methods:

Acupuncture.

Homeopathy.

Reflexology. (I mean, come on!)

Magnet therapy.

Naprapathy.

At some point in this process, I even considered sacrificing a goat to the gods of Valhalla.

I read every word, every sentence, every paragraph I could find on tinnitus on the internet. I tried everything and then some.

But you know what? It didn't make a bit of difference to my tinnitus at all.

At all!

The moral of this story is of course that if you are in the same spot now as I was then, please believe me when I say that looking for a cure is futile.

There is NO cure for tinnitus. I'm sorry, but that's the truth. And I will urge you NOT to spend even a penny/pence/euro/yen/rupee etc. on the thousands of remedies or "treatments" you find on the internet or elsewhere. It's all a scam.

Meeting Up With Other Tinnitusians

Time for a yet another digression. Let's jump into our time machine and travel to April 4, 2017.

This day, by chance, five of us tinnitusians at work had lunch together and the subject of tinnitus came up.

I hope this story from five tinnitus veterans will give you who are struggling a glimpse of what the future will hold.

The participants:

Roger: 58 years old, tinnitus since 1991, believes the cause is loud music, has (in his own words) the loudest tinnitus in the world.

Toro: 59 years old, tinnitus since 2001, has no clue where it came from, has (in his own words) *the loudest* and most fluctuating tinnitus in the world.

Jann: 60 years old, has had tinnitus since high school and doesn't know why or where it came from. He doesn't give a shit either way, but is sure that *his* tinnitus is louder than bombs.

Siri: 40 years old, tinnitus since 2010, says it came simultaneously as her hearing went from bad to worse. She *knows* her tinnitus is the loudest and most piercing sound in the world.

Me: Yours truly, 51 years old at the time, tinnitus since November 13, 2012. Tinnitus came out of nowhere while at work. And my tinnitus surely *is* the loudest and most high-frequency sound in the universe.

Scene: Lunchroom at the workplace. Five people bring their food to the table and start talking. Soon the conversation turns to tinnitus when one of the participants realizes that everyone around the table is a fellow tinnitusian.

Siri: "Jann here tells me that you have tinnitus as well. I never knew that."

Me: "Yeah. Was bitten by that little sucker a few years back. During the first two years, I thought I would just burn out. Lost all my will to live and all that jazz."

Siri: "Two years? Did it take you two years to habituate?"

Me: "Nah. Two years to learn enough about this wanker to stop believing my own faulty thoughts. It took another eighteen months before I got my life back, so to speak."

Siri: "Whoa! That's a long time. I was pretty much good to go in ten months."

Roger: "Ten months! Are you for real? I struggled with this nonsense for four years. On top of that, my doctor told me that it would probably get worse with age."

Toro: "That was reassuring of him. I must get his number. Didn't you get a second opinion? Or google tinnitus?"

Roger: "Google tinnitus? In 1991?"

Toro: "Good point."

Jann: "I can't even remember not having it. It has been with me for so long that if it suddenly went away, I would probably go mad with the silence."

Siri: "So you still hear it?"

Jann: "Sure I hear it. I can hear it even if I am standing right next to a waterfall."

Roger: "But does it still bother you?"

Jann: "Bother me? I don't think I have cared one way or the other since the early 1980s. How about you?"

Toro: "Not at all. When I first got this bullshit, I was convinced that I would suffer for all eternity, but I soon learned that my brain had to learn the ability not to treat it as a threat."

Roger: "Same thing here. It is one of the weirdest things I have ever experienced. After a year or so of ball busting depression and anxiety, it suddenly sort of... calmed down. Not the sound itself. It is still there, but my reaction to it. For me, it went away almost overnight. The reaction that is. Not the sound."

Siri: "I was convinced, no, scratch that; I knew that I had the loudest tinnitus in the world. I still do, but now I don't care about it at all. I mean, at all!"

Me: "But did you all experience that the first few months was the worst?"

Jann: "Worst? It was like hell on earth. I remember I just wanted to die."

Roger: "Agony. I was as miserable as can be."

Toro: "Worst time of my life. And I lived through some bad shit believe me. And I still have the loudest tinnitus in the world. Not like the baby-tinnitus that you people have."

Siri: "What? You have the loudest tinnitus, you say? I very much doubt yours can compare to mine."

Me: "Oh, shut up. You are as mad as a bag of ferrets the lot of you. I was a living wreck for over two years. None of you have any idea how bad my tinnitus is."

Jann: "But you are all right now, eh?"

Me: "Yes. I'm fine. I couldn't care less about it."

Roger: "Same for me. And I guess the same for all of us. No matter how bad it is or how long you suffer, you always turn out fine in the end."

Jann: "Yeah. And I don't think it even matters how you got it or why. The brain will eventually sort it out by itself. Because in the end, as you all know, it isn't a sound or a flaw in your ear. The sound we all hear is something our brain is manufacturing. For God knows what reason. But there it is."

Toro: "For many years I was chasing my own tail trying to cure this thing. All those years I was as useless as an accordion player on a deer hunt for my wife. There is no bloody cure. How can you cure a brain that is making noises for itself just for fun?"

Siri: "I probably wouldn't bother even if there was a cure. I have grown so used to it that it even comforts me from time to time."

Jann: "Like your own personal internal teddy bear."

Toro: "Spot on."

The moral of this story is, of course, that it doesn't matter how loud or how annoying your tinnitus is. It doesn't even matter how or why you got it. These are real people, who all, without exception, are living full lives with super-loud-screaming-bloody-murder-tinnitus. And they don't give a damn about it.

And before you start arguing that *you* are the exception. That *your* tinnitus can never be conquered, that *your* tinnitus and *your* reaction to tinnitus is different from everybody else's, let me tell you one thing.

You are wrong.

There is absolutely *nothing* special about your tinnitus. There really isn't.

The more I learn about this condition the more I believe that we all go through more or less the exact same thing. The only thing different is how we approach it.

Are we willing to learn from those who came before us or are we so stubborn that we simply refuse to leave our own little patch of quicksand?

Refusing to listen to reason and believing your own faulty thoughts will get you nowhere. But you will be all right. It just takes time and a whole lot of work.

The Turnaround

Back to the story. With the vacation over and done, I was back at work again and the familiar pattern from before continued: Two or three days in distress and one where I was mostly okay. Followed again by a couple of days of anxiety and depression. This cycle continued until Christmas when this Lovecraftian manifestation of a sound decided to hibernate for almost two weeks.

I was in heaven. I was convinced that my tinnitus was disappearing. During all of Christmas, I felt happy for the first time in over a year. I actually felt optimistic about the future.

Then, on January the 4th it came back with a vengeance. At this point, I wasn't even surprised. I knew the drill. On with the maskers, turn it up to 11 and start the descent into months of doom and gloom.

But something was different. I couldn't quite put my finger on it, but wasn't my reaction to the sound a bit...more relaxed?

I still had a great fear of the sound. I still felt the familiar feeling of anxiousness and depression sneaking up on me. But somehow, someway, the sound didn't have the same bite as before. It still felt like an almost physical pain in my head, but not as merciless as before.

What was happening?

I always think of my second year with tinnitus as a no man's land of endless back and forth. One week my tinnitus didn't trouble me as much, the next week it was back with a vengeance.

How come I felt so good during those two weeks at Christmas? I felt like the answer was staring me in the face, but I was never able to make eye contact with it.

How little did I know at the time? I was searching for an answer behind every nook and cranny. Much later I would learn that there wasn't even a question to seek solutions to, but at the time I was sure that there was a method to this madness.

Frode Singsaas

A Toothache, Tinnitus, and Paroxysmal Positional Vertigo

Fast forward to the summer of 2014 and we're off to yet another vacation. This time to Crete. I had now become a semi-professional tinnitusian, prepared for all eventualities. In my suitcase, I had packed mountains of hearing-aid-batteries. I had loaded up my smartphone with an assortment of white noise apps and in general, taken as many precautions as possible. I even brought a supply of foam plugs in case I should stumble upon some loud music (I've never heard of anyone "stumbling" upon loud music, but there you go, we tinnitus sufferers are anything but logical creatures).

I was looking forward to our vacation at that time. There was nothing (or so I thought) that my tinnitus could do that would surprise me. The only thing that was nagging me was a broken molar that had decided to get grumpy about things that came its way. I had postponed a trip to the dentist hoping that it wouldn't give me any discomfort during our week-long stay (and because I'm childishly afraid of dentists).

No such luck.

As soon as I sat my butt down in my seat, I instantly recognized the familiar feeling of a tooth that wouldn't take shit from anybody.

Great, I thought. Whoopty-fucking-doo! That was just what was missing. I decided to make an appointment with my dentist as soon as I got home. There was no way I was seeing a Spanish dentist (the workings of the Spanish Inquisition came to mind...).

Little did I know that this was just the first of two annoying conditions that would haunt me the rest of the week.

Later that day I suddenly felt dizzy. Not just a little dizzy, but really dizzy. I wasn't able to stand on my feet.

Okay, I thought. Now what? So, the toothache and tinnitus weren't enough? Fine. I can take whatever at this point. Even a little dizziness...

Then my head made a close encounter of the first kind with the floor. I simply dropped like a sack of potatoes. The room was spinning and I was spinning with it. It felt like I was on one of those teacups at the fun fair that go round and round in the opposite direction of the carousel itself.

A few minutes later I found that if I held my head at a particular angle and at a certain degree relative to the rest of my body, the spinning would stop. But if I tilted my head just a tad to the left or the right the spinning would start again.

After some time, the spinning finally stopped. I got up and crawled my way to the nearest sun bed. I was nauseous and drenched in sweat. Worst of all I had a nagging suspicion of what it was all about. While I was lying on the floor, doing my best to hold on for dear life, I remembered that my mother sometimes used to complain about spells of dizziness.

Frode Singsaas

Crystal sickness, she used to call it. A quick Google search led me to a website that had the answer: Benign paroxysmal positional vertigo.

The dizziness disappeared and three days went by without so much as a hint of it. I didn't think too much about it. After all, I had my tooth and my tinnitus to nurse in the blistering heat under the Mediterranean sun. Then it struck again. On the day before our departure home. While we were eating dinner in a crowded restaurant, suddenly everything went bat shit crazy. The tables suddenly took on some weird shapes, and the waiters all turned sideways and started walking on the walls. I bent forward and hid as best as I could under the table.

The reality was a merry-go-round, and all I could think of was not to vomit on the floor. I curled up under the table while my wife tried her very best to act as if nothing had happened.

"Sir. Are you alright?" A waiter asked.

"Yeah. I'm fine. Just lost my fork."

"Please, Sir. I'll get you a new one. Don't pick that one up, it is...but Sir. Your fork is on the table."

"Is it?" I said sheepishly. "My mistake. I was sure I...."

The waiter said something in Spanish and left.

"What did he say?" I asked my wife who has some rudimentary skills in the Spanish language.

"I'm not sure," she said. "But I think it involved you, a goat and some act of cunnilingus."

I looked over my shoulder. In the kitchen, I saw the waiter talking to some of his colleagues while sending me stolen looks.

"Let's go," I said.

"You don't want to finish up?"

"Nah. I need to lie down."

"That bad?"

I nodded.

The look on my wife's face as I held onto her arm as we were walking back to the hotel is something I'll never forget. Part fear and part distress. Her vacation has turned sour because of me. And there was no way either she or I could relax until I saw a doctor.

Two Incurable
Chronic Conditions

"No question about it," said my GP. "That's Benign paroxysmal positional vertigo for you."

"I guessed that much," I said, shifting uncomfortably in my chair.

"But will it go away?"

The good doctor shrugged. "Hard to say. Sometimes it goes away never to return. Other times..."

"It stays?"

He didn't answer.

"But it is related to my tinnitus? Or is it just one of those things that just happens?"

"Again, hard to say," he said. "I could refer you to a physiotherapist if you like."

"Will it do any good?"

Once more I was met with a shrug. "I really couldn't say," he said.

"For some reason, you have been blessed with two incurable chronic conditions. I wish I could be of more help, but...."

When I left the doctor's office, I was more depressed than I thought it was humanly possible to be. My ears were playing the complete back catalog of the German industrial rock band Einztürzende Neubauten and my balance system was having a drunken argument with a grumpy and out-of-date G-force simulator.

What had I done to deserve this?

Seeing the Dentist

Let me share a thing or two with you about my relationship with dentists. I grew up in the 1970s and 1980s. Back then, we had a school dentist: an underpaid dental professional from India who for some reason had decided that the backwater that was my hometown in Norway was *the* place to set up shop. This poor guy was not only responsible for the dental care for all 300 children at our school but also for an additional 300 students at the nearby high school. And as a bonus, his mastering of the language left much to be desired. His conversational skills were as follows: he either cracked a smile and said, "cavities," like he was some sort of archaeologist who had just discovered a long-lost tomb, or he wrinkled his eyebrows and said, "no cavities," and looked kind of sad.

I also must mention his method of filling a cavity. The procedure always started with the following question: "Anesthetic or no anesthetic?" Sometimes he didn't even wait for an answer before the drill was in my mouth. The few times he actually bothered to give me an injection it looked like he was paying for the stuff out of his own pocket. Needless to say, the treatment was both frightening and painful. And because this was in the late '70s and early '80s he treated every cavity as if it were a sinkhole. Every tooth became a crater in which he would pour as much amalgam as he could fit. As a result, my mouth to this day looks like a deserted quarry where you only can see some glimpses of white.

Since then every visit to the dentist was accompanied by the sense of a forthcoming apocalypse. But as my molar kept getting more and more painful, I no longer had much choice. My tooth was screaming bloody murder and I simply had to get it fixed. Add to this my fear that the drilling would make my tinnitus worse (suits me fine for reading horror stories about this on the internet), and the nightmare was complete.

But off I went. I had picked a dentist at random from the online phone register, and for once Lady Luck was on my side. It turned out that the dental industry had made some leaps since I last saw a dentist. I was greeted with a handshake and escorted by a stunningly beautiful assistant to the dentist chair (not in any way sexist; she was undeniably beautiful; I had to be blind not to notice). After some thorough examinations in which there was no discomfort involved, the dentist explained in layman's terms what needed to be done. My molar was broken and needed to be built up again. When I heard those words, I froze. I imagined expensive (and painful) root canal work and a price tag larger than the national budget of a small Asian country. But lo and behold, my fears and worries were in vain. In the course of just a few minutes,

Frode Singsaas

the dentist had built up my molar with some sort of white plastic, and my tinnitus hadn't as much as changed one iota.

"That was...something else," I said.

"It's been a while?" said the dentist.

"You could say that," I said. "I am terrified of dentists. Nothing personal, but I can't help it."

"Grew up in the '70s, did you?" he asked. And before I could reply he smiled and started to laugh. "You're in very good company."

Tonight, I'm adrift, conflicted, and in doubt,
I feel like a capsized boat,
and for all I suffer and moan about
I have found no antidote.
But why should I feel so rotten?
In one hundred years all is forgotten.
—Knut Hamsun

Bad and Good "Ear Days"

Summer turned to autumn and autumn turned to winter. My teeth were in mint condition and even my crystalline friend (that's benign paroxysmal positional vertigo to you) lay dormant most of the time. That meant that I could turn all my attention to my tinnitus in residence. I was now 18 months in to this, and still, I hadn't experienced as much as a fraction of this habituation-thingy everybody and their grandmother was talking about. I was still walking on eggshells most of the time and I was constantly aware of the sounds in my head. Truth be told, I had days when the cacophony of sounds was easier to deal with than others, but every good "ear day" was followed by at least two bad "ear days." Even worse, I couldn't find enjoyment in anything. Music, books, movies, TV-shows, all those things that had meant the world to me just a year and a half before were robbed of their meaning and enjoyment. I was the walking dead. A zombie. A shell of a man.

People with tinnitus often speak of good and bad "ear days." What this means (to them) is that some days the

Frode Singsaas

noise is more bothersome than others. Not necessarily bothersome as in louder volume, but in how high on the scale their anxiety goes.

At first, the bad "ear days" are more plentiful. They far outweigh the good "ear days." But the further along the road to habituation you get, the less you will experience them. As a rule, you should not dread the bad "ear days" even though you tend to feel worse on those days. They act as a token of the habituation process working its magic behind the scenes. Recovery, any recovery, seldom follows a straight line, and for tinnitus habituation, this rule applies double. But I digress, let's get back to the story.

And then without warning came Christmas (well, there was some warning, jingle bells all the way and so on, but you know what I mean).

The previous Christmas I was convinced my tinnitus was as bad as it could possibly get. I was wrong. Now it was worse. I was still paralyzed with fear most of the time, and I was still thinking about my tinnitus every second of the day. It was a case of Status Quo (the situation, not the band).

Like the ringer of Notre Dame, I covered my ears with my hands and groaned "the bells, the bells" every time I heard a Christmas bell.

Here I feel the need to interrupt the story with a word to the wise. This particular part of the habituation process was for me the hardest part. I was always online searching for success stories on the internet. Everywhere I looked I found people who had successfully habituated. Soon it looked like every tinnitus sufferer in the world could share a story about habituation and how good they felt. Me? I fell deeper into the pit of despair and malice and the world was a bleak and desolate place.

But on some days (on those aforementioned good "ear days") it was almost as if I could smell the habituation. In the rational part of my brain, I could somehow sense how habituation would feel, but the sensation kept alluding me. Why didn't it happen to me? I couldn't understand it. Why everybody else? Why not me? Why?

Now before I continue there are some truths about tinnitus that need to be repeated.

Most general practitioners out there know little to nothing about tinnitus. I know I have written this earlier in this book, but it is crucial knowledge when you are about to maneuver through the labyrinth that is the road to recovery.

Only a small number of tinnitus sufferers actually "suffer" from it. Most people who have ringing in their ears can continue with their lives without being bothered much by it.

It doesn't matter what kind of tinnitus you have. Some people with high pitched shrieking find it only mildly annoying, then, on the other hand, some people who just have a barely hearable "humming" in their ears freak out completely. There is no blueprint for this thing. There is absolutely nothing you or anyone else can "do" to make it go away, but there are different ways to cope with it.

And last but not least, the most important: people who don't have tinnitus or have not ever experienced it themselves won't ever understand what you are going through. I cannot stress this enough. I don't believe in ENTs, GPs or others who have not been where we are/have been. This is one of the things in life you have to experience yourself to make an educated statement about.

During my "lost years" (the first two years of suffering), I developed a myriad of bad habits. I can't possibly list all of them, but here's a little taster:

» Avoid loud sounds (it could make my T worse...).
» Avoid coffee, alcohol, and sugar (it could make my T worse...).
» Avoid people (they might talk loud and make my T worse...).
» Avoid loud music (it might make my T worse...).
» Avoid all music (because, well, you never know...).
» Avoid staying up late (it might make my T worse...).
» Avoid the alarm clock (it might make my T worse...).
» Avoid squirrels, bicycles, peanuts, curtains, donuts, cats, dogs, hamsters, trifles, waffles and...(because it might make my...well, you get the picture).

After two years this list was so comprehensive that there was literally nothing that I could do at all. Everything represented a threat to my tinnitus. Every sound, every song, every person, every everything. Of course, as I later learned, not one of those things made any difference to my tinnitus.

Let's recap the last sentence:

Not one of those things made any difference to my tinnitus. At all.

I can't stress this point enough. Of course, you shouldn't stand in the front row at a loud rock concert without earplugs or stick your head into the jet engine of a 747, but you know what I'm getting at. Use your common sense. It takes quite a lot of noise to make your tinnitus worse. Everyday sounds don't pose a threat to you in any way. Go about your life as if you don't have tinnitus.

If you are thinking (like I did) that there may be some truth in all those myths about tinnitus and coffee, wine, sugar, salt, pepper, red meat, chicken soup, licorice, oysters, sushi, broccoli, Christmas, summer, palm trees, sand, cats, chairs, etc., etc., ad infinitum..........you are wrong.

Most myths about tinnitus are just that, myths.

I read every word, every sentence, every paragraph I could find on tinnitus on the internet. I tried everything.

But you know what? It still didn't make a bit of difference to my tinnitus.

Try not to think about it.

This is the sentence you are most likely to hear from your GP or other well-meaning people of the goody-two-shoes affliction.

Try not to think about it.

This is, in my opinion, the most moronic thing you can say to a tinnitus sufferer. You can't help thinking about it. All the time.

But that's okay.

In the early stages of tinnitus, the sound in your head is all you can think about. The natural way to fight this is to try to think about anything but tinnitus. This is a strategy that you'll soon find futile. It's not the conscious you that leads your thoughts on to the sound, it's the SWAT team in your brain.

Frode Singsaas

The scene goes something like this:

Staff Sergeant: "OK. Listen up, people. We got a hostage situation here. An unknown entity has taken up residence in our host's head. Gear up. Assemble in T minus two minutes."

Private I: "Excuse me, Staff Sergeant. What do we know about the hostage taker?"

Staff Sergeant: "So far, nothing. No ID on the subject."

Private II: "Characteristics of the enemy?"

Staff Sergeant: "Uhm...it looks like he or she is invisible."

Private I: "Invisible?"

Staff Sergeant: "Yes, there has been no visual contact with the kidnapper, yet."

Private II: "So how can we be sure it really is a kidnapper, Staff Sergeant?"

Staff Sergeant: "Well, the host complains about an unknown intruder and the tension levels are sky high."

Private II: "So what are our orders, Staff Sergeant?"

Staff Sergeant: "Shoot on sight, boys. Shoot on sight."

Deployment

Private I: "I can't see a goddamn thing in here."

Private II: "Me neither."

Private I: "But the sergeant told us to shoot."

Private II: "At what? There's nobody here. Just as empty as its always been."

Private I: "But what about the sound?"

Private II: "What sound?"

Private I: "Well, if there is an intruder, he's bound to make a sound."

Private II: "You're right. OK. Everybody in position. We're gonna wait until the bastard gives himself away. Even if it takes all night."

The reason you're in such distress at this point is that there's a SWAT team on full alert in your brain. They're waiting in full preparedness, ready at a moment's notice to go all Rambo on the kidnapper. But the problem is that there is no kidnapper, there will never be a kidnapper. It's just this sound that isn't even a sound. So, the SWAT team will hold their positions and you will suffer the tension as long as they're there.

The noise that is driving you insane is made by one part of your brain, the SWAT team that is waiting in the shadows is sent out by another part of your brain. In other words, your brain is waging war on itself and it has no idea that it's a war it can never win.

If you are in the early stages of tinnitus and have just found this book, here's what I want you to do.

I want you to challenge your tinnitus. I'm perfectly aware of the fact that this is the last thing you want to do at this point in your habituation, but I want you to do it nevertheless.

Hang on. Did he say "my habituation?" But I don't habituate. Far from it.

But you do. You just don't know it yet. Anyway, we're gonna start off easy. And I'm not saying you should provoke your tinnitus. No, I want you to challenge it. And by that, I mean to challenge your perception of it.

How?

It's really easy. By now you should have a whole list of things that you are afraid of doing. It could be anything from listening to music with earphones to boarding an airplane.

Find the bullet points on your list that fills you with the least dread when thinking of it. We don't want you to freak out here, so go easy on yourself.

When you have decided on one or two things, take some time to yourself, make sure that you are in what you would consider a "safe tinnitus environment" (your home, office, or a similar place), then do the exercise of exposing yourself to the thing on your list that you are least afraid of exposing yourself to.

Sounds scary, doesn't it?

It is.

But it's a necessary exercise.

For the sake of argument, let's say that you are afraid that plugging in your electric guitar to your amp will make your tinnitus worse. In the past, you have been an eager amateur or professional musician, but the onset of tinnitus has left that part of your life stone dead. And it makes sense, doesn't it? To put that jack plug in the Telecaster and crank the volume up to 11? It makes sense that fifteen minutes of shredding will make your ears bleed, so why shouldn't it provoke your tinnitus?

All I'm saying is give it a go. Play at a moderate volume. Not too loud, but not too low either. Do it like you used to do. You know, back when you had a "life" and you knew the meaning of words like *happy* and *content*.

I promise you that nothing will happen. Your tinnitus will stay the same and you will find that you get a small sliver of joy from playing again.

This is a baby-step. And you will be doing a whole lot of these in the months ahead.

Most tinnitus sufferers lose all interest in previous interests and passions after the onset of this condition. Especially everything that has anything to do with sound is suddenly a no-no for most of us. And it's only natural. We have a sound in our heads that makes us anxious, afraid and depressed, so why wouldn't we avoid everything that has to do with what makes us suffer.

But all these are external sounds. Tinnitus is an internal sound. And the two have nothing to do with one another, strange as it may seem.

Food is also a typical no-no for tinnitus newbies. Most of us who suffer experience weight loss faster than a Japanese bullet train speeds through the landscape on its way from Tokyo to Kyoto. Not only do we lose our appetite for life, but also our appetite for all things we previously loved to stuff our faces with.

And although most of us are not afraid that food or drink will make our tinnitus worse, we still are not able to work up an appetite. Not even for our favorite dishes. But we have to eat, so I suggest you develop a new strategy. Learn to cook something you always wanted to try but never thought you would pull off successfully. Make it an exotic and difficult dish. What will happen is that you will be so concentrated while cooking that you will forget all about that sound in your head for minutes at a time. And as an extra bonus, you will have learned to cook something extraordinary both for your family, your friends and for yourself.

This is how you do it. Never rush yourself. You have all the time in the world right now. Baby-steps. Always remember baby-steps.

Interlude

Right now, I'm sitting by my kitchen table, typing these words. My head is a tropical storm of different noises. A few years ago, I would have called this a very bad "ear day." Today it doesn't bother me at all.

Right now, you are pacing the room while reading this. Your head is a polar storm of disturbing noises. This is a very bad "ear day" for you, and it bothers you to no end.

How come we both experience the same perception of noises in our heads, but only one of us is *suffering* from it, while the other one is entirely at ease with the same thing?

Habituation.

I have habituated to the sounds in my head. You have not.

But you want to.

Right?

You so desperately want to.

But you have convinced yourself that the sound in *your* head is very different from mine. Furthermore, you've convinced yourself that even though many people get better, *you're* the exception. The medical anomaly that never will habituate.

Frode Singsaas

You are wrong. And I say this with absolute confidence. You are wrong and I know you are wrong.

And I will prove it.

To speed up the process of habituation, I strongly suggest that you start the healing process with the baby-steps mentioned earlier. You will get there no matter what, but a little helping of baby-steps will not only speed up the process, it will also make it more fun.

So, what do you say? Are you ready to follow my journey a bit further?

Read on, dear reader, and I'll share with you the story of what happened on a sunny morning in May, 2015.

"A melancholy-looking man, he had the appearance of one who has searched for the leak in life's gas-pipe with a lighted candle."

—P.G. Wodehouse

Method to the Madness

One beautiful morning in May, when the birds were singing that old Beatles song "And Your Bird Can Sing," and the sun gently woke me from my slumber, I noticed that something was...different (why the birds chose to sing a song about singing birds puzzled me, but I let it slide, I had more pressing matters to attend to).

With my wife off to work and my son on his way to school, I picked up the phone and called in sick. I was determined to get to the bottom of this strange sensation.

With the house to myself, I turned off everything that made any noise and locked myself in the bedroom. I sat on my bed and listened.

"ZZZZHHHHHIIIIIISSSSSSSUUUUUUUSSSS!!!" Said my tinnitus.

"SHHAAAAAARKKKKKGOBBLEGOBBLEHYE-NAAAAAAAAAA! CLUCK-CLUCK-CLUCKETY-CLUCK-TWEEEEEEEEET!!!!!"

No, everything was in its right place. The Great Cthulhu was back in his lair, happily rummaging about, probably do-

Frode Singsaas

ing some house cleaning (I even recognized the sound of his vacuum cleaner, a Nilfisk Saltix 10).

The pitch, the volume, and the noise were exactly as they first appeared that November day in 2012. But it didn't sting anymore.

It didn't hurt me. And it didn't scare me.

Wait.

What?!

Stop the press!

The noise didn't scare me!

How come? How was it possible that the very sound that made me a crying wreck of a human for the last couple of years now appeared almost...innocuous?

The myriad of feelings and thoughts that washed over me at that precise moment was almost too much. My tinnitus was making its usual racket but, somehow, I felt perfectly calm. For the first time in two years, my stomach wasn't a knot of anxiety. And for the first time in two years, my heart was beating at its normal rhythm.

I don't know how long I sat on the bed, analyzing every little nuance of this new feeling. Slowly I started to perform a checklist on myself.

Was I anxious?

No, I wasn't.

Why wasn't I?

I had no idea.

Was the noise in my head the same as it ever was?

Oh, yeah. And then some. I could hear and feel that I was having a bad "ear day" but for some mysterious reason, I didn't seem to react to it.

Was I still feeling depressed and blue?

No, I wasn't. I felt fine. And all of a sudden, I had a strong urge to do several things at once. Things that used to be my passion two years previously, but had gotten buried under this brick wall of fear and anxiety.

I wanted to sing, I wanted to dance, and I wanted to read a book, watch a movie, play the piano and eat myself to oblivion on pizzas, hamburger, steaks, and sushi.

But most of all I wanted to get naked and run out into the street, lifting my arms to the sky singing hallelujah.

Was this the moment I had been waiting for?

Was I...habituated?

But of course, the moment couldn't last. The second I stepped outside my bedroom, the familiar feeling of dread and gloom overtook me once again.

Aw, come on!

Confusing Moments

The following week, my head was occupied with the following questions:

Why did I experience a moment of absolute bliss?

Why did I experience a moment where my tinnitus didn't seem to bother me at all?

Why were my anxiety and fear gone for a moment?

Why didn't it last?

Was it something I did? Did it have something to do with me sitting on my bed? (I tried to recreate that moment. It didn't work. Sitting on your bed for 30 minutes during a sunny morning is mind numbingly boring.)

During the following week, I experienced some happy moments. But they'd never last. I was sure it meant something, but what?

I was reminded of Paul Davis' book on anxiety.

"It's okay to allow myself to feel miserable," I said out loud to myself.

I decided to try to analyze all the conflicting feelings inside me that were fighting with each other. It was a confusing mix of relief and fear, but I was determined to separate them and hold them up to scrutiny each and every one.

First, there was the joyful, but the enigmatic feeling of actually having experienced the loss of fear and anxiety for a significant amount of time. What could it mean? Was it a taste of things to come (I was very wary of this, fool me once etc.) or was it just a fluke?

Then there was the return of the fear and the anxiety. Was it as dominant as before? I closed my eyes and tried to connect to these feelings. No, it wasn't. I was still scared of the sounds in my head, but I also noticed that my fear had sort of lost its edge. Like a boxer whose punches gets weaker towards the end of the match.

Finally, there was this feeling of certainty. This had to mean something. Furthermore, it felt like there was a new "button" inside my brain. A button that when I pushed it diminished all those negative emotions that were attached to my tinnitus. It was very mysterious.

Yes, it was okay to feel miserable. I got that. But what if I couldn't manage to feel as miserable as I was used to feeling? Because, no matter how hard I tried to wallow in my misery, this time, it simply wouldn't stick.

Frode Singsaas

Tinnitus is an Invisible Condition

As mentioned before, non-tinnitusians have a hard time grasping what tinnitus really is. Nor do they understand the almost abstract kind of suffering that comes with it. Here's an example of a typical conversation between a tinnitusian and a non-tinnitusian.

"Noise in your head? Where did it come from?"

"Hard to say. It just appeared out of nowhere."

"But what does it sound like?"

"Even harder to say. There are multiple sounds. One that sounds like that static sound that we used to hear from old CRT-TVs. Another sounds like a deranged banshee. The third one sounds like a 747 revving its engines."

"All these simultaneously."

"Yeah."

"All the time."

"Well, some of them I can hear most of the time. A few of them comes and goes. They fluctuate."

"Loud?"

"Painfully loud. I can hear it over anything. Except for the shower. Don't ask me why."

"But there isn't any physical pain?"

"No, not as such, but...."

"So why don't you stop listening to it?"

"Stop listening to it? It's impossible. It's like an alien entity attacking your skull."

"You are such a baby about this. It is just a sound, isn't it?"

"Yes, but...."

"I wouldn't care if I heard a sound in my head."

"Of course, you wouldn't...."

"You said it yourself. It's just a sound. How bad can it be?"

But if it were "just a sound" tinnitus wouldn't be a condition that pushes people to despair. It wouldn't be a condition that alone is responsible for the annual turnover of millions of dollars, pounds, euros, yen, and many other currencies every single year for snake oil and miracle cures. There has to be more to it than "just a sound."

And of course, there is. The sound itself isn't the problem. The problems are the fear and the anxiety. They are the stowaways that come with the shipment of tinnitus.

Tinnitus is one of those conditions that's hardest to understand if one hasn't experienced it first-hand. Anybody can relate to pain. Everybody can relate to having a cold, the flu, or a toothache, but only those who have had tinnitus can connect and truly understand how it feels to have these annoying sounds in your head every single second of every single day.

This notion became more apparent to me as I inched my way through the first year of tinnitus. Tinnitus is an invisible

Frode Singsaas

condition. Nobody can look at you and say, "Oh, I see you have tinnitus. I'm sorry for you."

And even if you do your best to remind both family, friends, and coworkers that you struggle with this, they tend to forget it as soon as they turn away.

All this is easily understandable. Remember, unless you are crying your eyes out and continuously complaining about the noises in your head, you look just like any other person. And it's not like they can hear the noises in your head, is it?

Tinnitus is a lonesome condition, and the struggle is one you have no other option than to take on yourself. But it is also important to remember that you are not alone. Hundreds of thousands of people all over the world struggle with this condition. And every day thousands more join their ranks.

The Thunderous Nap Syndrome

Sleep has a different effect on every tinnitusian. The majority struggle most at night when it is time to sleep. However, some lucky few find that the sleep is the only escape from the ever-present sound in their heads and that they are capable of falling asleep quite easily.

This was me. I was able to fall asleep quickly even during my worst suffering. As soon as the freak-out phase was over (three-to-four months after the onset of tinnitus), I usually fell asleep just a few minutes after my head hit the pillow—something that in my case was a mystery only comparable with mustaches on eggs. You see, all my life I have been an insomniac. Not the sort that never sleeps, but the one who usually tosses and turns for at least a couple of hours before the Sandman finally came knocking. I believe the medical term for this is sleep onset insomnia.

But lo and behold, once I was deep in the nightmarish reality of tinnitus suffering, my chronic sleep disorder vanished. During the first two years of tinnitus, I slept like a child. Of course, when I woke up every morning, it was a different story altogether.

But the strangest thing was that every night just before I fell asleep, my tinnitus would disappear altogether. It still does.

The first time it happened I almost jumped off my bed, ready to scream that my tinnitus had disappeared. But as soon as I sat up, the noise was back. This happened every night without exception. After some time, I learned to treasure those moments—just a second or two before I drifted off there was complete silence.

I have spoken to others who also experienced this bizarre condition. Nine out of ten tinnitus sufferers seem to suffer from insomnia in one form or another. It comes with the territory. But for the tenth person, it is the opposite. They sleep like babies the moment their heads hit the pillow.

But I digress, the title of this chapter is "The Thunderous Nap Syndrome" and every sensible reader will at this point ask him or herself when this slightly infamous nap will take center stage of the narrative? A very reasonable question. So, without further ado, let's hear it for the nap.

One of the most terrifying things every tinnitusian discovers about this condition is the way it presents itself after sleep.

I've interviewed a lot of people with tinnitus for this book, and without exception, they all have horror stories to tell about that first nap after the onset of tinnitus. Here's mine.

A few days after the appointment with Dr. Evil, I had an extraordinarily busy day. At this point, I was still conflicted about what to do about my work situation. I had been too confused and scared about the whole thing to even think about asking for sick leave from Dr. Evil. In the back of my mind, I knew that sooner than later I had to make some sort of arrangement with my employer. But I had just received the message that the noises in my head for sure was tinnitus, so I just kept pushing all thoughts of practical arrangements to the back of my mind. The suffering alone was more than enough to occupy my every waking moment.

The day started with a busy schedule of meetings and workshops followed by a workday that never seemed to end. After work, I had to drive to school to pick up my son. And on this particular day, my son informed me that he (ecstatic with anticipation) had invited his best friend to eat dinner with us. At this point, I had been up since 4am and was already exhausted. But I kept my head up, drove home and started on dinner. One hour later both boys were fed and were playing happily with the Nintendo Wii. As I let myself slump down on the sofa like a beached whale, I heard the Sandman whisper the sweetest words I've ever heard in my ear.

"It's OK," he said. "They're not going anywhere. Look how they play. Just close your eyes for a second. You deserve it. You're right here with them should anything happen."

"But I have to do the dishes," I tried to reason. "And the cat needs the litter in the litter box to be changed, and the clothes need to go in the dryer...."

"Shhhh," said the Sandman. "It's just for a few minutes. And you will feel like a million bucks."

"But, I can't..."

"Shhhh..."

I fell asleep. For approximately five minutes.

"Dad, can we have some ice cream, please?" My son's voice woke me up.

Frode Singsaas

A crazy loud noise penetrated my skull. A thousand chain-saws chopping away at rusty railway tracks accompanied by an Italian mezzo-soprano singing at the top of her voice.

"Uh, sure. Just go ahead," I said with the taste of sleep still on my teeth. "You boys get whatever you want. OK? Daddy's just gonna go to the bathroom for a minute, yeah?"

"Ice cream!" Before I even finished the sentence, they were racing for the fridge.

In the bathroom, I looked at the reflection of myself in the mirror. I looked like a madman. I looked scared witless. But my appearance was of no importance to me. The only thing that I was able to think about was the sound in my head.

It was like nothing I had ever heard before. It was agony.

I can't go on like this, I remember thinking to myself.

I fell to the floor and cried like a baby.

Tinnitus is always worse just after waking up. Especially from daytime naps. Something I learned the hard way. I didn't dare to take a nap after that incident for almost three years.

The thing is, every time we wake up our bodies are per-forming a check-list like a check-up for your car. Are the batter-ies okay? Check. Enough oil? Check. How 'bout the oil filter? Good to go. The same thing happens when we wake from a nap or after a night's sleep. But in the case of the tinnitus suf-ferer, our internal mechanic soon finds the faulty component.

And what does he do? He alerts the person the body be-longs to and tells him or her to fix the problem ASAP.

But of course, you cannot comply.

These days I nap anytime I can. I love naps. And the sound in my head when I wake? I no longer hear it. My brain filters it out. And even if it raises a ruckus, I couldn't care less.

On Setbacks and Why They Are So Important

So, what are setbacks? Setbacks are periods of time (be they months, weeks, or days) where you feel worse than your bog-standard lousy tinnitus day. The most typical aspect of a setback is that you feel like you are back at square one—that all the progress you have made (or falsely convince yourself that you haven't made) has been for naught. Setbacks are periods of time when you are certain that you feel worse than the periods that preceded them.

You may feel worse, but you are recovering.

Let's repeat that.

You may feel worse, but you are recovering.

Sounds a bit far-fetched, doesn't it?

You have to think of setbacks as a part of the healing process. It is just like getting better from a cold or the flu. One minute you feel fine, the next you are feeling like an old dog.

There are no healing processes that follow a straight line. There are ups and downs all the way. With tinnitus, it's the same thing.

Frode Singsaas

Think of it like this: When it comes to tinnitus, your brain is quite dumb. One day you are feeling quite good and saying to yourself that "OK, maybe this isn't so bad after all. Right now, I'm feeling rather good. I must be getting better."

The next day your brain has forgotten all about this feeling and is in red alert-mode once again. This makes you think, "Oh my God! Why am I feeling so miserable today? I felt so much better yesterday. I'm never gonna get better!"

Relax. This is the brain working its way out of this terrible place you are in right now. It takes time for the brain to stop treating tinnitus as a threat.

Do not be afraid of setbacks. Setbacks are a sign that your brain is trying to solve this problem by itself. And it will. But it takes some time.

You cannot trust your thoughts at this point. Your thoughts are faulty. Period.

Allow yourself to feel down. Allow yourself to feel depressed. There is no use trying to "fight" these setbacks. They will occur no matter what you do.

You do get better after each setback, but not in the way you think of as "better." The healing process goes on behind closed doors, so to speak. And the conscious part of your brain is not allowed to take part in it.

Think of it as a battlefield. After the battle, the field is littered with dead soldiers.

Your brain is your battlefield and the setbacks are the dead soldiers. There's a war raging and you feel like you are losing. But here's the thing, the part of your brain that is fighting for habituation might have lost the battle and will lose many battles to come, but it won't lose the war.

You simply have to be patient and wait it out. One day you will wake up and say to yourself, "Hmm...I'm having a setback today, but for some reason, it doesn't bother me as much as it used to."

That's when things start to pick up speed. Sadly, no one can tell you when this will happen. Most commonly it happens between eight to sixteen months after the onset of tinnitus, but don't freak out if it takes you longer. Remember, there are no rules to this game. Everybody habituates at their own speed. Putting a time frame on your habituation is the most dangerous trap you can fall into. Tinnitus exists outside of time. Think of that part of your body and mind as a parallel universe where time works differently. Your day might be 24 hours, but you can bet your grandma's dentures that "tinnitus time" is something else entirely.

The good news is that you *will* come out on the other side as a better and happier person. It happens to us all. It is inevitable. The brain will stop seeing this sound as a threat and when this happens you couldn't care less about your tinnitus.

As I am sitting here my own tinnitus is having what I would call a bad "ear day" or a "setback" in the old days. I couldn't care less even if I tried. It doesn't bother me at all. Most of the time I can't even hear it (even though I know it's there).

This will happen to you as well. Most of the time someone who has habituated to tinnitus has to *search* for the sound. Like tuning a radio to the right station. But remember—always remember—these things take time. And when it happens, you will not only get your old life back but a whole new life. A life where you suddenly can appreciate things that you never took the time to enjoy before.

Frode Singsaas

It may not feel like it, but setbacks are your body's way and your mind's way of telling you there is a healing process going on in the back room. You just haven't been invited to the party.

Although setbacks are most commonly categorized as periods of bad "ear days," it can for some mean a new sound or an increase in volume. In my experience, every tinnitus sufferer has their own interpretation of what a setback is. For me, it was the return of the fear and anxiety after a period when I had felt more or less like my old self.

The irony of it all is of course that concepts like good and bad "ear days" will only be understood by people who suffer from tinnitus. For everybody else, such terms will not only seem indecipherable but also slightly comical.

I strongly believe that setbacks are simply emotional flashbacks. They are a tug-of-war between the rational part of the brain and the part that controls emotions.

Always remember there is very little that can be considered established in tinnitus research. There are many papers that suggest *many* places in the brain are involved in tinnitus but so far there's no one single conclusion to what tinnitus really is and what's causing it. It's easy to lay the blame on noise exposure but what about the millions of tinnitusians who've never been to a rock concert, or worked in a noisy environment, or otherwise never been exposed to loud noise?

You could scour published research data for days accumulating clues on how and why tinnitus just occurs in some people but you will never find one single answer, just a myriad of contradictory theories.

Flashbacks are also when your body and the emotional part of your brain "remember" the fear and anxiety from the freak-out phase. The good "ear days" that now seem to be more frequent, are a direct reaction to when the rational part of your brain manages to shut down the red alert button.

After the episode in the bedroom, I started on what I like to call the *no-man's-land-of-one-step-up-two-steps-back*. Every day was like a lottery. Would it be a good "ear day" or a bad "ear day?"

A good "ear day" meant that I would hardly pay my tinnitus any attention at all. The fear and anxiety were gone, and I would function as I did before the onset of tinnitus. Those days were filled with hope for the future and I was optimistic to an almost manic degree.

On the bad "ear days" I felt I was back at square one. How could I be so foolish to think that I was on my way to habituation? How could I possibly be so dense as to think I was able to live a happy life with this miserable bastard living in my skull?

Every night when I went to bed, I wondered what the next day would be. Would it be a day with happiness and joy or would it be a day with misery and dread?

It wasn't *like* night and day. It *was* night and day. One day my tinnitus didn't bother me at all, the next it was all over me like a hungry vampire. And it drove me half mad. I could not fathom how I could have all these conflicting feelings and thoughts.

What puzzled me to no end about this period, was how it was possible to hold so many conflicting feelings? And why didn't the good "ear days" last?

It would be funny if it weren't so sad, but this *no-man's-land-of-one-step-forward-two-steps-back* lasted almost two whole years.

Frode Singsaas

But I knew I was onto something. I could feel it. I just couldn't make sense of it at the time. But as I later learned, the never-ending conflict between my rational side and my emotional side was the habituation at work.

I believe now that setbacks are when your brain and your body suddenly "remember" the fear and anxiety from the early days of tinnitus suffering. You have no other choice than to go through the emotions. Logic and reason do not compute when the flashbacks occur. The feelings are so much stronger than logic.

But if there is one valuable lesson I've learned from the endless setbacks during my years in the *no-man's-land-of-one-step-forward-two-steps-back* it's this:

Habituation works exactly like love-sickness. At first, you are devastated and your emotions are playing blackjack with your soul. Only later are you able to reason (in small doses) until finally, that old heartache is just a distant memory.

When Bad "Ear Days" Turn Into Good "Ear Days" And Then Just "Days"

Just before Christmas 2015, something weird and wonderful happened. I still had my good "ear days" and bad "ear days," but somehow my bad "ear days" weren't as bad as they used to be. In fact, they were merely a nuisance.

This change happened pretty quickly. From the end of November 2015 to the end of March 2016 my bad "ear days" had turned into not-so-bad-"ear days." From there on out until summer 2016, my tinnitus simply stopped bothering me.

"Aha! But that's because your tinnitus changed," I hear you say.

Nope. Nix. Njet. My tinnitus didn't change at all. It was still screaming bloody murder, and the deranged banshee in my skull was still doing her very best to get my attention. But my feelings for her were dead.

"So, what you are saying here is that in a few months your tinnitus just stopped bothering you? The same tinnitus

Frode Singsaas

that had made your life a living hell during the previous three years? You seriously want me to believe that?"

Well, yes. I know how it sounds (no pun intended). And believe me, nobody was more surprised about this than me. But let's rewind a bit. What did happen during that three-month period between Christmas and Easter?

The first thing that I noticed was the disappearance of anxiety. The fear of having a bad "ear day" was still present when I awoke most mornings, but the tension, the ever-present feeling of dread had somehow faded out. It still lingered somewhere in the perimeter of my consciousness, but it was no longer as persistent as it had been. For the first time in over two years, I felt...*optimistic*. For the first time in what seemed like two lifetimes, I had the urge to do something. I wanted to go to work, and I wanted to get out of bed and see what this strange new day had in store for me.

A few hours later I suddenly remembered that I had not thought about my tinnitus at all since getting out of bed.

What a glorious feeling. For something that felt like eternity I had done nothing but nursing the thoughts about my tinnitus all day—every day. Now, for some inexplicable reason, it was gone from my mind. It was the same feeling I had experienced the summer before when I sat on my bed and felt the fear and anxiety vanish into thin air. Only this time I knew that it wasn't just a one-time occurrence. I knew that this time it meant something. The beginning of a process that would escalate by itself. I could feel it in my heart, my bones and in my mind.

The next day I woke up with the familiar anticipation of how my day was going to be. It was going to be a bad "ear day" for all practical purposes, but yet, I still felt good about it.

I feel good about feeling bad, I thought to myself and allowed a slightly hysterical laughter slip through my lips.

"What's that, old dog?" My wife asked puzzled.

"Oh, nothing, dear," I said. "Just something funny that I thought of."

She mumbled something incoherent and went back to applying mascara on her lashes. She didn't pursue the subject any further.

Good. I didn't want to jinx my good fortune by declaring myself on the road to habituation. I wasn't even sure this was the road to habituation. As far as I was concerned, I had had two days without the choking anxiety that had been my trusted companion for over two years. Needless to say, I was reluctant to actually trust in this newfound feeling of relief.

But the strangest thing was that this lifting of my previous state of mind and body just kept going. Every day when I woke, I braced myself for the inevitable setback that I knew would come, but lo and behold, it never did.

Soon the fear also let go. And by the end of May, I woke up for the first time without any trace of fear in my mouth. All that was left was the sound of old Mr. Tinnitus Sourpuss doing his thing. At this point, the sensation of actually hearing my tinnitus and not reacting to it in any way, was so new to me that several times a day I had to find a place of privacy and enjoy the feeling of it all.

Relief and Amazement

By the end of summer 2016, I knew I had this beast beaten. For over six months I hadn't experienced any significant setbacks of fear and anxiety. There had been days when my thoughts once again turned to the doom and gloom that once was my whole life, but they seldom lasted. And as summer turned to autumn, my determination easily conquered even the hardest days. Nothing could stop me from living my life to the fullest ever again.

I was finally free of the tinnitus monster.

Now, if by this point in the narrative you feel slightly confused about just how this came to be, I understand. This process is hard to understand and explain. But what happened was my brain finally stopped treating my tinnitus as a threat and started to focus on other issues.

And do not for one minute believe that the sound, the volume, or the pitch of my tinnitus had changed. Not at all. But my attitude towards my tinnitus had changed. For some mysterious reason (well, not so mysterious actually, it is called plasticity, it is a natural part of us as humans, and I'm sure you can find hundreds, if not thousands of boring documents about it both off and online), I just didn't care anymore.

When you habituate to your tinnitus, you stop caring if it's there or not.

Bloody marvelous, isn't it?

I guess you don't believe me? That's OK. When I read similar statements during my freak-out phase I didn't believe them either.

"Bollocks!" I used to mutter under my breath. "The people who write such nonsense don't have the same disturbing and super-loud tinnitus that I have."

Oh, but I do. We all do. Everyone who gets hit by this truckload of strange noises believes that without a doubt their tinnitus is the loudest and most unbearable tinnitus in the history of the universe.

You are both wrong and right. Nobody but you knows how loud your head noise is. I was convinced that I was a special case—the one tinnitus sufferer that would never habituate because my sound was so intrusive and loud.

Later I learned that almost all tinnitus sufferers think this way about their tinnitus.

In 2004, the American author John Irving published a children's book by the title: *A Sound Like Someone Trying Not to Make a Sound*. What a great title. For us tinnitusians that is exactly what we all try to do during our first few months.

We skulk around the house, trying our best not to make a sound because we so desperately need to monitor our head sound. We are "The People Who Are Listening for A Sound

That Doesn't Exist." And it is a booming sound. A roaring silence that occupies our every second of the day and the night.

We obsess over this sound, and we cry because of this sound. The sound is us, and we are the sound. There's nothing else in the world. Us and the sound, the sound and the fear.

Later, the sound is still very much the same, but we have changed. We no longer skulk in the shadows, desperately monitoring our inner demon. There is so much more in the world that we want to do instead. We want to smell, taste, feel, and experience. The sound that drove us nearly mad has now become "The Sound We Couldn't Care Less About."

And that's magic in my book.

Nobody believes in habituation when they are suffering. The thought itself is too surreal. It's like hyperopia (far-sightedness which tends to show up after a certain age). It's a thing we accept as we grow older and we never expect it to improve by itself, so we compensate with glasses or lenses.

It's the same thing with tinnitus. When we are in the claws of the tinnitus monster, the thought that we one day will shed all the anxiety, fear, and misery is surreal. We cannot imagine a future when the sound in our heads doesn't mean anything to us. It's a leap of faith that our fear-stricken brains won't let us make.

But unlike the ways we adapt to hyperopia, and a million other irreversible conditions, tinnitus habituation is unique when it comes to improvement of its underlying condition, and this is where "moments" come in.

This is what is guaranteed to happen to you:

You have been wallowing in misery, fear, anxiety, and depression for...let's say a year and a half. So far you haven't experienced even one millisecond of this habituation you've been reading about.

But then something happens. And you don't notice it until it's gone. While you were doing the dishes back then (or any other mundane task), wasn't there a minute, just a minute where you were unaware of your tinnitus? For just a very, very short moment in time?

Nah. That can't be. Surely you are mistaken.

But then it happens again. Perhaps several weeks later, and this time you know there was a moment. Maybe just a few seconds. A short period when you didn't think about or were even aware of your tinnitus.

Pure bliss.

This is how habituation works. Like a thousand small streams that all flow in the same direction and eventually make a river.

Tinnitus habituation consists of these moments. And in the beginning, they are few and far between. But gradually you start to notice that they happen more often. And then you begin to see that they last longer.

And then you start to think that maybe, just maybe there is some truth in this after all.

You have hope.

Then the hope is lost because you suddenly feel like day one. The fear and anxiety are back again with a vengeance.

But then you have these moments again.

Then the setbacks.

Then the moments.

Then the setbacks.

Then the moments. But this time you are sure that they last a bit longer than the first ones you had. You will experience times when these moments will last for hours, even days.

Holy jumping George! There is some truth in this habituation thing after all. You know it. You can feel it. You can even taste it!

Then one morning, months, maybe years after that very first moment when you did the dishes and forgot all about the sound, you sit up in bed and feel the strangest sensation known to man: your tinnitus is screaming bloody murder as usual, but you don't pay any attention to it. It bores you. Instead there are a thousand different things you suddenly feel like doing. Things that you used to take pleasure in, but haven't even considered doing for the longest of time, because of, yeah, tinnitus. But right now, sitting on your bed, your tinnitus doesn't bother you anymore.

This is the moment where all those tiny moments have turned into the river. And it's like magic.

This is what habituation is all about—those fleeting moments that are so deceptive.

A Very Short Chapter about Medicine

I didn't use any pharmaceuticals during my "lost years" as a tinnitus sufferer. Nothing at all, even though I was prescribed antidepressants after my second visit to my GP. But I never took one single pill.

As I have later learned this is quite uncommon for a newbie tinnitusian. But I was determined to get through this ordeal without any pharmaceuticals. I had seen close family members ruin their lives at the cost of antidepressants and other forms of benzos. And I was dead set on never becoming addicted or even accustomed to the use of medicine in any shape or form.

I do not doubt that antidepressants are a perfectly fine way to cope with the fear and the anxiety that come with the onset of tinnitus, and I would never be judgmental of anyone who chooses to ease their pain through medicine.

It just wasn't for me.

And that's all I have to say on the subject (as I said, I would talk very little about medicine, so there you go).

Frode Singsaas

Samantha's Story

So, I got through the winter, the spring, the summer, and the autumn. Suddenly it was Christmas again. It was now a year since I had any fear or anxiety attached to the sound in my head. As mentioned before, the sound, the volume, and the pitch were the same as it had been since day one, but I no longer cared. But all through 2016, the sound of my tinnitus was the first thing I heard when I woke up every morning. That too had an end. On Christmas day I rose to what would turn out to be a beautiful day. It had snowed all night, and the city was a mesmerizing globe of pure white snow and blinking lights. With almost childish anticipation for what the day had in store, I jumped out of bed and headed for the bathroom. While I was brushing my teeth, I had this nagging sensation that I had forgotten something. But I couldn't for the life of me get a hold of what it was.

During breakfast half an hour later, it hit me. I hadn't noticed the state of my tinnitus when I woke. How come? It was the first thing I always noticed. Even during the whole previous year. Even though my tinnitus didn't bother me anymore, it still was a significant part of me. And as you probably know, tinnitus is always at its most wicked in the mornings. But this particular morning I hadn't even noticed.

How come?

I lay down my knife and fork (but not without a longing glance at the half-eaten plate of pickled herring, smoked ham, and scrambled eggs) and went to the bathroom where I shut the door and started to listen.

Could it be that...?

No, of course not. My tinnitus was the same. "O come, all ye faithful. Joyful and triumphant," it croaked with its Gremlin-like voice. It was there, all right. Same as it ever was. But how come I didn't notice it when I woke?

This pattern repeated itself during the next six months. The days when I woke without noticing my tinnitus multiplied, and the days when I was aware of my tinnitus diminished. Soon I noticed I had to listen for my tinnitus to even hear it actively. By the time winter once again turned to summer I could count the days when I noticed my tinnitus in the morning on one hand.

Make no mistake. The sound, the volume, and the pitch during all this time were exactly like they had been since the dreadful day when I was convinced the fire alarm went off at my workplace five years prior.

"ZZZHHHHHIIIIIIIIISSSSSSSUUUUUUUSSSSSUUUUHHHH!!!!!!" says my tinnitus. "SHAAAARKKKKKGOBBLEGOBBLEHYENAAAAAAAAAA!

C L U C K - C L U C K - C L U C K E T Y - C L U C K T W E E E E E E E E T - Z O T H - O M M O G - S H U B - N I G G U RATHZZZZ!!!!"

Frode Singsaas

"Oh, put a sock in it!" I usually reply nowadays. "There's nothing you can say or do to make me feel miserable. How about I make you feel miserable?"

I then shut my eyes, press the invisible button in my head, and the sound of my ever-present tenant melts away. My tinnitus has no power over me anymore.

Nothing he (mine's a "he," perhaps yours is a "she?") can do or say makes the slightest difference to my well-being and happiness. The same thing will happen for you.

You just have to be prepared to suspend your disbelief on a few things. And one of those things is your own perception of the truth.

You see, the *truth* for a tinnitus sufferer isn't necessarily the objective truth. Let's use "Samantha" as an example. Her tinnitus appeared around the same time I considered myself somewhat habituated.

Samantha has had tinnitus for 2½ years and is desperate to get her life back while being simultaneously obsessed with protecting her hearing. She is convinced that any noise or sound could potentially make her tinnitus worse. Because of this conviction, she feels constantly on edge and often unable to relax among other people. Samantha describes her tinnitus as "annoying and frightening, on the border of being unbearable." Her greatest fear is her tinnitus becoming louder.

As a result of this, Samantha avoids leaving the house and withdraws from family duties and family life at a steady pace. Samantha is a first-grade teacher and because of her fear of tinnitus getting worse, she has taken a medical leave from work, but she's constantly worrying about the day when she's expected to go back. The thought of any children suddenly screaming in her ear is making her a nervous wreck.

Samantha has even stopped going to the mall or the grocery store for fear of any loud sounds. She categorically says "no" to any invites from her friends and is slowly losing her social network.

Samantha is about to isolate herself completely, convinced that any sound is a potential threat to her tinnitus. Lately she has stopped listening to the radio or watching TV. She's able to identify her behavior as obsessive-compulsive, but is powerless to break free from the pattern that is encapsulating her.

Samantha is convinced that her thoughts and fears regarding her tinnitus are correct. Her feelings tell her they are correct, and Samantha has no reason to doubt her own feelings.

Like Samantha, I also trusted my feelings. Why shouldn't I? After all, our instincts are part of the very same defense mechanisms that have allowed us to survive as a species. When our brain warns us about an immediate danger, our instincts tell us to run and hide. We seldom, if ever, question this instinct because we have no reason to.

But in Samantha's case (and for every tinnitus sufferer), trusting one's instinct is counter-productive because it's a warning about something that isn't a threat to us. Reversing this part of our DNA-programming is not an easy task and requires a suspension of disbelief.

Like Samantha, I also had an "inner expert" who told me what to fear, what to do, and what to avoid. The result of listening to my inner voice was almost three years spent in a constant state of fear, anxiety, and suffering.

When tinnitus was new, I believed every thought and every feeling I had about it. Just as Samantha does. And why wouldn't I? Who knew better than I did about my own experience? It took close to three years to accept and understand that, in the case of tinnitus, my thoughts and feelings were not to be trusted. It was my own thoughts on tinnitus that had caused me to feel so utterly miserable. Of course, during these three years I had heard and read from numerous sources that this trust in my own thoughts and feelings were faulty. But still I refused to listen. How could my experience be *wrong*? How could I not trust my own misery?

This is what Samantha is struggling with now. She has been given the same set of information as I had, but because her tinnitus experience is still new, she struggles to make sense of this information. She knows she's in distress and she cannot understand how she can start to disbelieve the very thing that she feels or thinks.

Only when our brains start to treat the head sound as a minor threat and not a major one, will the idea of not trusting one's thoughts and feelings find a small foothold. But once the foothold is established, there's no going back. Your perception of your tinnitus will change, no matter how hard you fight it.

Six Hard-Earned Lessons on How to Cope With Tinnitus

"Really?! You waited all this time before you came to the only thing worth reading?" You say, "Who gives two slices of burnt toast about your 'tinnitus journey?' We want to know how to get rid of this noise in our heads."

I'm sorry to say that most likely you will never *get rid* of the noise in your head. But I can assure you that the alternative to getting rid of the sound is just as good.

While researching this book, I've met, talked to, and written to dozens of habituated tinnitusians. Some have had this condition for decades, others for only a few years. But they all have one thing in common—none of them have the slightest problems with the ever-present sound in their heads today.

All of these people experienced the habituation process in their own way, but the outcome was the same for each and every one of them—the noises in their head stopped causing fear and anxiety, and they got their lives back to normal.

Almost half of all the tinnitusians I talked to had never heard the term *habituation* before and knew nothing about

Frode Singsaas

the plasticity behind it. Yet they all claimed that over time they had gotten used to the sound and stopped obsessing about it.

Getting used to the sound is just a layman's term for habituation. The process is always the same. You stop obsessing over the sound and slowly your life gets back on track.

So, what to do while you are waiting for the habituation process to start? How to best cope with the sound(s) that make every waking minute miserable?

There have been volumes written about coping mechanisms both on tinnitus and other issues, and I won't get into details about the science behind all the different approaches on how to deal with physical and mental difficulties. Instead, I will list the most common (in my opinion) ways of coping that you can apply to your own tinnitus journey.

1. "Cum On Feel The Noize."

Like that old Slade-song from 1973, you should put some time into finding the right masking noise for your tinnitus (if you choose to go down that road). If you own a smart phone, the world is your oyster in this regard. Both the App Store and Google Play have a wide variety of white noise apps. Some of them cost money, but most are free. Download a whole bunch of them and see if you can find a noise that matches the pitch and the tone of your tinnitus the most.

When the going gets tough, you need to find a private spot for yourself and listen to your sound of choice on the phone for a few minutes. Not only will this help you calm down, but it also lets you "not hear" your own head noise for a few minutes. In my experience, this can do wonders.

A word of warning here. I will not advise excessive use of this method for hours at a time. It is only meant as an instant relief. In the long term, you have to train your brain to get used to the sound of your tinnitus, so consider this method as a sort of band-aid to stop the bleeding after a paper cut.

2. Take a shower.

This one worked best for me. The sound of running water, and especially the shower, completely masked my tinnitus. Not only that, but it also had a lasting effect. A shower could turn my bad "ear day" into a good "ear day." To this day I have no idea of how or why this happened. As far as my research goes, approximately 60% of all tinnitus sufferers experience a soothing effect by listening to running water.

3. Think baby-steps.

This is perhaps the most crucial piece of advice. If you, like me, felt that your life was taken away from you with the onset of tinnitus, you have also lost your ability to appreciate the things that you had a passion for and interest in. Be it clubbing, music, literature, movies, TV-shows, gaming, exercise, shopping, or whatever used to tickle your fancy. What most of us tinnitusians discover after the onset is that our previous past-time favorites no longer hold any fascination. We now not only have to learn how to live again but also how to learn to love the things we used to love.

All this may sound excessive, but it's a disturbing side effect of tinnitus that we lose not only our ability to appreciate silence but also all those things we used to care about.

All these things need to be taken back and returned to our lives. And the way to do it is by baby-steps. You have to force yourself to go out. You have to push yourself to enjoy music again (this one's particularly tricky because everything you listen to now must pass through a veil of hissing and screeching noises) and in a similar vein, you also have to force yourself to socialize again.

All these things take baby-steps. You must learn to take your life back, one little thing at a time.

4. Stop feeling sorry for yourself and instead do something for others.

Another essential step. In my experience, tinnitus sufferers are the most self-centered people on the planet. Not surprisingly, perhaps, because every waking minute we concentrate on how we can get rid of this noise. But alas, wherever you turn, you find indifferent answers and puzzled looks.

What you need to do is turn your attention away from yourself and onto others in need. Volunteer to help at a soup kitchen, keep yourself busy with computer aid for senior citizens, or turn all your attention to your spouse and kids and surprise them every day with an exotic meal or a day at the zoo. Soon you will find that you are having so much fun doing those things that you no longer have the time or the energy to obsess over your tinnitus like you used to.

5. Tinnitus is not the end of the world as you know it.

Sit down. Pour yourself a glass of your favorite brew and think about it. What is tinnitus? It is a sound. A sound in your head. In no way does it pose a threat to you. Annoying? Yes, but it's not a hazard to your health. Start to think about all the conditions and illnesses that exist. There are so many incurable diseases in the world. Everyday, people die of cancer, diabetes, Ebola, AIDS, and countless other diseases.

Will you die from tinnitus? Not a chance.

Then there are the diseases and conditions that will leave you paralyzed, comatose, and crippled. The only thing your tinnitus will do (worst case scenario) is rob you of your ability to hear certain frequencies.

You won't die from tinnitus. You won't be disabled, paralyzed or comatose. This is just a bump in the road we call life, and if tinnitus is the worst bump you'll ever come across consider yourself the luckiest person on the face of the earth.

6. Don't believe the lies.

The first thing all of us do when we get hit by the tinnitus monster is to go online and seek answers. And why not, your GP didn't have a clue what it was all about and your ENT probably told you there was nothing to be done about it and that it probably only gets worse as the years go by.

So, you go online to find comfort. What you are most likely to encounter are thousands of people who are in the same distress as you and are desperately seeking answers. Here you'll be advised to stop drinking coffee, eat enough Ginkgo Biloba to sink a supertanker, and to sacrifice a newborn goat at midnight to the gods of the underworld.

And, as most of us who have habituated already know, all this boils down to nothing. To find one sensible piece of information on how to cope with tinnitus, you have to plow through ninety-nine pieces of misinformation. The internet is full of desperate people who are trying their best to make sense of this deranged banshee in their skull.

It is then you notice all the ads. Ads that promise relief from your pain. Ads that promote herbs and jumbo-sized pills that can "cure" your tinnitus. Ads that offer you soundtracks that will make you forget the sound in your head. Don't believe the lies. So far, there is no cure for tinnitus. Perhaps it will come some years down the line, but as of now there is none.

Frode Singsaas

It's a Journey

First, let's get one thing straight. Habituation is not an end game. It is a journey. You'll never be fully habituated, you are always habituating. Nevertheless, we use the term to *be habituated* because how can you still be habituating if you no longer care about the Cthulhu-monster in your head? That's because the same mechanisms in your brain are still at work.

When I first noticed that I no longer cared to obsess about my tinnitus, I thought that this was as good as it gets. A year later, when I hardly thought about my tinnitus at all, I was sure that I had reached the end of the line. Then at Christmas last year I was dead certain that this was it, I had finally achieved full habituation. Tinnitus suffering was now a fading memory, a sort of dream in the back of my mind. Surely now I had achieved total habituation! But it just kept going.

I can now sit in a perfectly quiet room and summon my tinnitus like a teenager tries to invoke a spirit with a Ouija board. Sometimes he is shy and won't come forward. Other times he tries to trick me with an ambush, pops out and screams his usual nonsense in my ear. When he does, I laugh at him.

"Is that the best you can do?" I ask. "You have to try harder than that."

"I'm gonna make your life mizzzerable," he croaks. "I'm gonna make you hurt. I won't ever leave you in peazzzzz. I'm gonna zzzing zzzongz of darknezzz and dezzzpair til the cowzzz come home. You're gonna wish you never were born. Becauzzze I am your tinnituzzz and I'm never gonna leave."

"Oh, clam up!" I usually reply and enjoy myself by totally ignoring him.

This is habituation in a nutshell. When the fear and the anxiety have lost their grip on you and the *no-mans-land-of-two-steps-up-one-step-back* is just a speck in the rear-view mirror, you get your life back and then some.

And it is glorious. It feels fantastic. But not just for me, also for you, and for every tinnitus sufferer out there. You may think that I'm dead wrong on all of this, and you may think that my journey is mine alone, and you may think that none of this applies to you.

It does apply to you.

Habituation is real.

Don't just take my word for it. Take it from the millions of other tinnitusians out there who got through this and got their lives back. I'm aware that there are many who disagree with me, people who refuse to believe in the scientific facts and empirical evidence of habituation. Scared, anxious and desperate people who will take nothing less than a complete absence of their tinnitus as a satisfactory end to their suffering. People who will advocate for pharmaceuticals, alternative medicine, stem cell therapy, homeopathy, acupuncture, reflexology, and whatnot as the only effective treatments.

Frode Singsaas

This book is not for them. This book is for you—the brave soul who dares to face this beast head-on without aid from witch doctors or voodoo priests. You, the one who is desperately trying to make sense of this bizarre condition that has fallen upon you.

To conquer your tinnitus, you must surf the great rapids of hardship and coast on the small streams of relief—cherish them—even if they only last for a second. Eventually, like a river, these moments will flow together.

You'll be right as rain. That's a promise.

About the Author

Frode Singsaas is a journalist for *Adresseavisen*, which was first published on July 3, 1767, making it the oldest Norwegian newspaper still in publication. He's also a moderator for the Tinnitus Support Message Board (TSMB). He currently lives in Trondheim, Norway.